Return to Lilacwell

Sasha Morgan lives in a village by the coast in Lancashire with her husband and has one grown up son. She writes mainly contemporary fiction, her previous series having a touch of 'spice', probably due to all the Jilly Cooper novels she read as a teenager! Besides writing, Sasha loves drinking wine, country walks and curling up with a good book.

Also by Sasha Morgan

Lilacwell Village

Escape to Lilacwell
Return to Lilacwell

Sasha Morgan

Return to Lilacwell

CANELO

First published in the United Kingdom in 2023 by

Canelo
Unit 9, 5th Floor
Cargo Works, 1–2 Hatfields
London SE1 9PG
United Kingdom

A CIP catalogue record for this book is available from the British Library.

Print ISBN 978 1 80032 961 4
Ebook ISBN 978 1 80032 960 7

Cover design by Diane Meacham

Look for more great books at www.canelo.co

Printed and bound in Great Britain by Clays Ltd, Elcograf S.p.A.

1

For Alex, my everything.

Chapter 1

A crowd was starting to gather on Goldgate Square. This leafy quarter of north London, with its artisan shops, deli, wine bar and even barristers' chambers, was certainly not accustomed to such vulgarities as a 'demo'. The activists remained huddled together united, brandishing banners of 'save the earth!', 'stop the emissions!' and 'tunnel to triumph!'

Interest in the spectacle was quickly building momentum, as news reporters started to land on the scene. A transit van pulled up. Two people scurried out, a man carrying a TV camera, the other a lady holding a furry microphone. They hustled to the centre of the commotion, elbowing their way through, only to come to a sudden stop at a well-dressed man standing confidently in front of the otherwise motley crew of protesters. He was tall, broad-shouldered and had unmistakeable presence. Dark, unruly curls covered his bright blue eyes, which he kept sweeping back as he spoke clearly, eloquently and with passion.

'These people are defenders of the earth. They are not intent on martyring themselves. Their sole intention is delaying, or even stopping the dual carriageway project.'

'The Transport Secretary calls them reckless, irrespons-ible and deeply concerning!' one reporter called out. To this, the man turned his blazing eyes on the reporter in question.

'By the government's own admission, it will be heavily polluting and carbon intensive, while demand for mass transit is falling and home working is the new norm for many people. It simply cannot ignore the climate crisis.'

'So will you be in the tunnel with them?' asked the lady with the microphone, shoving it in the man's face.

'No,' he replied calmly, 'I'll be in court defending them.' He pushed his way through the throng of people and, with his head held high, walked calmly into Goldgate Chambers, leaving the reporters all gobsmacked.

He was greeted with cheers and claps by a few barristers, while others kept quiet, exchanging anxious looks between themselves. It was all well and good being the saviour of the earth, but how would this debacle make their chambers look? Goldgate Chambers held an extremely high reputation. It represented the rich and famous, the great and the good (and the not so good). What light would this young maverick of a barrister cast on them?

'Well said, Rory!' shouted one. Another slapped him on the back. He took it all in his stride, just nodded his head in acknowledgement, then strode into his office.

Once inside he sat down and buried his head in his hands. Damn. What had he done? Had he sacrificed his entire career, one which he had worked so bloody hard to achieve, for his principals?

For Rory Molloy was indeed a man of principal. He had morals and, up until now, had no problem at all in standing up for them. He had honour, and was ready to fight for it. But had he gone too far this time? Had his mature, more experienced colleagues been right when they'd warned him against representing the activists? At the time he'd laughed it off, claiming he was actually one of them. But he wasn't laughing now. Far from it.

It had always been this way with Rory. He was impetuous, passionate and a *doer*. He'd headed the student union at university, his strong, persuasive voice often forcing change where it was needed. He spearheaded rallies and was often seen plastering some flyer or other in public places. Rory knew how to attract interest. His good looks and charismatic personality made him forever popular with the ladies – not that he craved that kind of attention; he simply wanted his voice to be heard. He wanted to make a difference.

He laughed to himself; he was most definitely making a difference today. Who would have expected a well-groomed, well-spoken young barrister to speak up and defend what some would call a bunch of hooligans? And for free, as Rory wasn't charging the protesters. He was acting for them because he believed in what they stood for. To him they *were* defenders of the earth. They *did* have a point – and a very good one at that. So, it wasn't costing them a penny. But would this cost him? Would his wise, older counterparts be proved right? Had he in fact pushed the boundaries with too much vigour?

'Typical Rory,' said Adira, turning the laptop on the breakfast bar to show her fiancé. Jasper bent his head to see for himself. He took in the scene at Goldgate Square and chuckled. 'He was always one to support the underdog.' She shook her head. 'I hope this isn't his undoing though,' she added quietly. Adira had worked in Goldgate Chambers as a barrister alongside Rory. They'd hit it off immediately, both being the most down to earth of them all, and Rory had proved to be the biggest friend amongst a nest of vipers when she had had the guts to finally follow her dream and ditch the rat race.

After several years of running the fast-paced legal tread-mill, Adira had opted out and taken off in a campervan, making her, if not the most enviable, then the most puzzling of colleagues. She'd received mixed reactions from, 'Good on you!', 'Wish I had the back-bone,' to '*Why?*' To some, quitting a high salary, prestigious career and bountiful future was absolutely insane. Wasn't she now reaping the benefits from those impressive qualifications she'd earned after years of hard work and long hours? They simply didn't get it. When Adira had tried to explain how she desired time, space and freedom, they'd just looked blankly at her. Yet, for Adira, it had been the best decision of her life and she didn't regret it. For, on her travels, she'd found love; she'd found Jasper. Glancing at him, she thanked her lucky stars – or rather, her gran for persuading her to buy the campervan. Jasper was the polar opposite to her, but that's why they worked. He was her rock, her anchor, together with his uncle in whose house, The Laurels, they all lived.

The large Georgian country house sat on an estate in a beautiful, quintessential village, nestled in the Forest of Bowland in Lancashire. When Adira had practically stumbled upon this quaint place, filled with quirky characters, she'd instantly fallen under its spell. Lilacwell had bewitched Adira, and she'd grown to love the place and its inhabitants. She'd grown to love Jasper, too. In turn, Jasper had been smitten by the pretty young woman, with long blonde hair and beguiling smile, who had parked her campervan on his uncle's land. And now, several months later, here she was, engaged to be married to him.

'Do you think this could have repercussions?' asked Jasper, nodding his head at the laptop still showing the mass of activists outside Goldgate.

Adira shrugged. 'I hope not. But that chambers did have some very unsavoury characters and Rory was never one to keep his opinions to himself.' She pictured Rory locking horns a few times with one or two of them. Richard, the office manager in particular. Not to mention the Head of Chambers, Nigel Kerfoot, who she had always considered to be a touch creepy.

'Maybe he's better off without them then,' replied Jasper. He remembered first meeting Rory a few months ago when he'd come to their summer party. Rory had expressed how good it was to be back up north, as that's where he was from.

'Perhaps he would. Rory refuses to conform, that's his trouble.'

'Oh, I don't know,' grinned Jasper, 'a certain someone seemed very interested in the old rebel.' He was referring to Cassie, Adira's friend, who worked at the local pub, the Inn at Lilacwell. They had struck up a bond immediately when Adira worked there temporarily.

Rory had sought Cassie out amongst their party guests and the two had seemed to hit it off. Somehow, though, nothing had materialised. Adira didn't like to pry, but did think it a little odd that Rory hadn't pursued her.

Jasper got up from the bar stool and hugged Adira from behind, dropping a kiss on the top of her head.

'He could always buy a campervan and clear off like you did, sweetheart.'

Adira lent back into his chest, loving the secure, warm feeling of his arms wrapped round her.

'The best decision I ever made.'

'It most certainly was.' Jasper nuzzled into her neck and squeezed her.

Chapter 2

Cassie flicked off the TV and took a deep breath. Taking a few moments to steady herself, she glanced at the clock. She was due to start work soon so didn't have time to dwell on what she'd just seen. Thank goodness.

Mentally shaking herself into action, she got up from the sofa and nipped to the bathroom to put on a touch of make-up, where she gazed at the reflection before her. She sighed, noticing how pale she looked, then applied some blusher and lipstick. There, that was better. Then she ran a brush through her pixie cut until the chestnut hair shone. Not bad, she told herself, before making her way downstairs to the bar. She was on lates tonight, so wouldn't finish her shift until after eleven p.m. As assistant manager of the Inn at Lilacwell, it was up to her to make sure the place was closed securely last thing at night.

At least she didn't have a journey home to make. Living in the hotel was convenient in many ways, yet inconvenient in others – such as being permanently on call. Not that it bothered Cassie too much, for she loved her job. However sometimes, like now, after seeing Rory on the news, she craved a little piece and quiet, a sanctuary where she could stop and take stock. Had she made the right choice? That low, sick churning sensation began to settle in the pit of her stomach. Again.

Before she had chance to dwell, she switched on her best friendly front-of-house smile and began serving and chatting to the locals. Here was her safe place, comfortable in familiar surroundings doing what she did best – being the hostess with the mostest. Cassie knew every nook and cranny of the Inn and all its punters. It had been her local pub, having been brought up in the village, and after obtaining a degree in hotel management, Cassie couldn't think of a better place to be than the Inn at Lilacwell. She hadn't been tempted to stray to the bright lights of a city, it had simply never appealed to her. Cassie was a home bird. Unlike many her age, she totally appreciated her roots and where she came from. Being born in an area of outstanding natural beauty had been a privilege to her and she'd vowed never to leave it, a country girl through and through. She craved the wide, open space of the lush green fields and the trickling of spring water. She loved nature trails with the family labradors, swimming in the babbling brooks and cuddling up to crackling inglenook fires. The whole country life suited her down to the earthy ground she walked on.

Only once had she ventured out and momentarily considered another way of life. But that was history now. Justin was an ex-boyfriend who lived and worked in London, having now made quite a name for himself as a hedge fund manager. He was ambitious and had wanted Cassie to share his lavish lifestyle in the city, with a promise that once he'd made his fortune, they'd settle down in the country. But Cassie realised early on that was never going to happen. Justin was not going to give up his high-flying career, his flat on the Thames, his Porsche or his Champagne Charlie friends, to stay put in a cottage in the middle of nowhere with her. She'd grown tired of the long trips to London, packed on a train filled with commuters, to visit him and she'd grown tired of waiting for him to join her in Lilacwell. In the end she did the sensible thing and called the relationship off. From then on Cassie had made a conscious decision – no more long-distance relationships.

The trouble was, all the locals were spoken for. Every farmer had a wife it seemed. So, when a certain tall dark stranger approached her at Adira and Jasper's party, Cassie thought her luck was changing. He had an easy confidence, not in an arrogant way, but more natural and charming. He made her laugh and she was genuinely interested in his job as a barrister. Then came the bomb-shell – he lived in London. She'd blinked when he'd told her. He had a northern accent, so she'd assumed he was a friend of Jasper's from Cumbria. When Rory explained he was in fact Adira's friend and they'd worked together in Goldgate Chambers, Cassie's heart sank. Not again. From that moment her defences came up and she found herself suddenly inventing a boyfriend – using Justin's details, because the best lies are grounded in truth, right? – who couldn't make it to the party. A prickle of guilt stung her at the disappointment on Rory's face, but he seemed to take the hint and soon made his excuses to move on.

Throughout the night they'd catch each other's eyes every now and then, but neither made the effort to talk again.

Convincing herself she'd done the right thing still hadn't stopped her from looking him up on the Goldgate Chambers' website though. There he was looking devil-ishly handsome, complete with a mischievous grin, making his cheeks dimple. Apparently he specialised in human rights and had a long list of letters after his name.

Cassie had been quite surprised because he most definitely had not come across as pretentious, which many would if they had similar qualifications. All this had truly piqued her curiosity; Rory Molloy intrigued her and the more she researched him the more interested she became. Often, she would go on the chambers' blog and follow what he was up to – a lot, it appeared. Rory was forever fighting one cause after another and his latest had caught the attention of the national press, and now hers.

After a long, hard but enjoyable night, Cassie eventually turned the lock on the hotel front door and heaved a sigh of relief. Her feet, back and shoulders ached. She was desperate to relax in a hot, deep bubble bath. The added bonus of living in a hotel was the luxury of a huge roll-top bath with Molton Brown toiletries. Tonight, Cassie decided to have a drink of wine to accompany her soak. After an hour of utter indulgence, she wrapped herself up in a fluffy bathrobe and sat on the edge of her bed. Her eyes homed in on the laptop sitting on the bedside cabinet. Unable to stop herself, she reached out and opened it up. Clicking on the BBC news page she searched for the report on the Goldgate Square activists and there Rory was once more. She played the footage and heard his voice.

'These people are defenders of the earth...'

Cassie stared, taking every detail of him in. The way he swept back his hair, as he spoke so valiantly, a real hero. That wretched pain came back, twisting her insides. A dull realisation ate away at her. She'd messed up.

Chapter 3

Fletcher Hendricks eased into his favourite chair. He was in the drawing room sat by the open fire, enjoying its warmth as he gazed into the dancing flames. He found it therapeutic. He could hear his housekeeper, Lilly, in the kitchen with Classic FM playing gently in the background. Soon she'd be joining him for a mid-morning coffee. Simple pleasures, he smiled to himself, but weren't the best things in life free? For him that was certainly the case – all Fletcher had to do was compare this time last year to be reminded.

Lilly had been the one to alert his nephew to the startling state of affairs; at eighty-five, Fletcher was struggling to manage The Laurels and its estate. Although Jasper had practically been raised there, and as the closest relation to him would inherit the lot, he had been living in Dubai for a few years and hadn't realised the extent of his uncle's decline. On returning to Lancashire, he saw for himself just how much he was needed there on the estate, so set about plans to move back to Lilacwell. Of course, this all coincided perfectly with his new-found love, Adira.

Together they had transformed the beautiful, yet rundown country house, giving it a new lease of life. Jasper, having a good, sensible business head had whipped the estate into shape too. Fields were now harvesting, orchards producing fruit, tenants paying rent and together with Adira, they had set up The Laurels Hideaway, a glamping site on their most picturesque field by the river. Adira's campervan took pride of place, as a flagship to illustrate how the venture originated.

Fletcher would be eternally grateful for Lilly's intervention. Often he would consider how things may have panned out, had she not. He shuddered at the thought of him being a lonely old man, left to cope alone in a huge empty house. While he loved The Laurels – of course he did, it was the family home, passed on from generation to generation – it also meant inheriting its problems and the astronomical cost to upkeep it. As the years had tumbled on, so had Fletcher's health until he was riddled with arthritis and his bones didn't half bloody ache. Whereas once he'd enjoyed surveying his land, chatting to tenant farmers and discussing matters with his estate manager, it all became such hard, hard work. He still took pleasure in his blessed vegetable garden, but even that had taken its toll; all that bending and digging had left him in pain and useless for anything else. In a nutshell, it had been well and truly time to pass on the baton – and who better than Jasper to take over.

Jasper was his pride and joy. He'd been a big influence in his life from birth. Indeed, Uncle Fletcher had had much more of an impact on Jasper's life than his own parents. Summer holidays had been spent at The Laurels with Fletcher filling the little boy's days with fun and excitement. Foraging in the forest, fishing in the river, camping in the woods – huddled together as they toasted marshmallows by a fire under a starry sky. Uncle Fletcher had a knack for storytelling, often leaving a young Jasper in hysterics. Every summer holiday was the same, full of joy and laughter, but inevitably had to end. Watching a sad little boy made to pack his suitcase with tears in his eyes had always broken Fletcher. Gritting his teeth, he had hugged his precious nephew hard, with promises of Christmas coming soon. Even now, when reminiscing those times Fletcher still filled up.

But it was all different now. Lilly *had* alerted Jasper and he was here, permanently. Would Fletcher be around to see Jasper's children grow up in The Laurels? He bloody hoped so! There was life in the old dog yet, of that he was sure. Which brought him nicely to his next thought: Lilly. Not much younger than himself, he thought she well and truly deserved a break. They'd always been good friends, having been brought up together. Lilly had secretly worshipped Fletcher from afar, and had been more than happy to help out at The Laurels when his housekeeper had up sticks and gone. Truth be told, it was more companionship than anything else they both needed, so the arrangement suited. Lilly would pop in and do the ironing, or wash a few pots, then together they'd sit and chat.

Fletcher though, in his wisdom, wanted more. Whether it had been Jasper and Adira living with him that had put a spring in his step, he wasn't sure, but a new lease of life he most definitely had. And, as such, wanted to share it with Lilly. She had been his most loyal and faithful friend.

He pulled out the brochure from the side of his chair. A river cruise, that's what he'd decided upon. Why not? He pictured him and Lilly sailing along the Danube, sipping cocktails, exploring Budapest, Slovakia and Vienna with their medieval history and gothic architecture; cruising through picturesque wine regions, with the wind in their hair and not a care in the world...

'Fletcher, tea break!' chimed Lilly, interrupting his thoughts. In she came carrying a tray.

'Ah, Lilly, come and sit yourself down.'

'There we are.' She passed him a cup and saucer.

'Thanks. Lilly, I've been thinking, let's get away for a few days, go on a little holiday.'

'A holiday?' She looked at him in alarm, like he'd gone mad, slowly sitting herself down on the chair adjacent to his.

'Yes. A holiday. Why shouldn't we?' She paused to think. Not waiting for an answer, Fletcher continued with gusto. 'Just think, me and you, Lilly, being pampered in luxury.'

'Well… yes I suppose—'

'We deserve it!' he barked. 'At our time of life, after all we've been through.'

'I know where we could go,' clapped Lilly, soon adjusting to Fletcher's way of thinking.

'That's the spirit,' replied Fletcher, beaming.

'How about Blackpool?'

Dear God, she really did need pampering.

'Hmm, how about something a tad more adventurous?' he said gently, passing her the brochure.

Chapter 4

Rory was reaching fever pitch. He was used to pressure, but not so publicly as this. Wherever he went people were either congratulating or challenging him, be it at work, home or just out and about. Journalists started to follow him. A small camera crew had set up quarters in Goldgate Square, wanting to catch the most up-to-date news on the activists, or any sight of the barrister representing them.

Of course Rory had invited the publicity. It's what he fully intended – to get the climate issue plastered on the front of every newspaper and on TV screens. But he hadn't quite anticipated the attention it would bring to him *personally*.

It was starting to impact on his everyday life. He couldn't go out of his flat without being confronted. He struggled to get out of the chambers too and had even taken to disguising his appearance by wearing dark glasses, a beanie hat and exchanging his smart black overcoat for a denim jacket.

The whole episode was creating quite a stir. An uncomfortable atmosphere hovered in the chambers. Rooms went silent each time he entered them, followed by smirks, awkward coughs and occasionally the odd snigger. It seemed everyone had an opinion. The commotion had split into two camps. Rory was either a 'warrior for the earth', acting as a champion for the climate, or he was 'an irresponsible, arrogant showman', fighting a losing battle. Which camp his own chambers officially fell in remained to be seen. Truth be told, they were all watching and waiting for a sign from their Head, Nigel Kerfoot, to take the lead and show them what the party line actually was. But their Head of Chambers was a slippery eel who hadn't decided himself. For he, as ever, was desperate to keep Goldgate Chambers in the best possible light. If Rory won the pending court case, then he would be cast a star, an absolute trooper for the climate cause. But, if Rory lost, then he would undoubtedly have tarnished them all with irreparable damage. Rory Molloy would forever be linked to Goldgate Chambers – they'd never shake him off, soiled by association. It was a real quandary. So following his instincts – if in doubt, do nothing – Nigel Kerfoot was waiting like the rest.

In the meantime, tensions were rising and Rory was suffering. He hadn't slept much, he was drinking more and was in need of a break. He knew the activists had started tunnelling beneath Goldgate. A number of the protesters were digging, while the rest were busy creating a commotion on Goldgate Square, to deflect attention. How did he know this? Because that's what he had advised. Rory had deliberately chosen Goldgate Square as the best place to summon up the most interest. It was busy, easily accessible and not far from where the proposed dual carriageway was to run. More importantly, it housed his chambers. Rory wanted the cameras to witness him enter Goldgate Chambers and give the activists credence, so they could be taken seriously. Seeing a barrister defend them would give gravitas and make it less likely for them to be treated as a 'bunch of hippies' making a nuisance of themselves.

The tunnellers were in Goldgate Gardens, positioned at the far rear of the square, behind a stone wall, where part of the new road would cover. Once it became apparent, the construction company would step in with measures to stop them. They would take legal action, aggravated trespass for a start, possibly criminal damage. Rory needed to be ready when they did. He'd spent days (and nights) preparing for it, weighed under by the stress of potentially letting down the protesters. He had convinced them that he could fight their corner, not that they had been inundated with top-class barristers representing them free of charge. But even so, he had an obligation and was anxious to fulfil it to the very best of his ability. He wasn't scared about losing face, because for him he never could. Despite what anybody else might label him, *he* firmly believed in his actions. Technically, Goldgate Chambers couldn't throw him out on his ear, but they could make things so difficult for him that he'd choose to leave. So what? he thought. He wouldn't want to work for such an organisation in any event.

It was at times like this he envied Adira. At least she did have the gumption to up sticks and leave. And look how happy she was now! His thoughts turned to her and Jasper's summer party – and more importantly the girl he'd met there. Cassie. He hated the fact she'd got under his skin. Even worse, he hated the fact she was off limits. She had a boyfriend and Rory, being the gentleman he was, had quietly walked away, but that hadn't stopped him looking her up on the hotel's website.

Rory stared at his screen. The office was empty. Nowadays he purposely waited until later when it was quiet outside to leave the chambers. Tapping the keyboard, he was soon on the Inn at Lilacwell's webpage.

He sat back and admired the view. Such an idyllic setting. What he wouldn't give for a piece of that.

> The Inn at Lilacwell is an old-fashioned rural Inn, welcoming to all, providing 23 bedrooms of some glamour, seriously good local ingredients cooked well and a note-worthy selection of drinks. We aim to offer a relaxed and friendly service.

He longed to breathe clean, country air and not the relent-less smog of the city. His limbs ached to stretch out and run through the verdant forests, up grassy hills and along clear running streams. His body also ached for something else and holding that thought, he opened the team page. There she was, Cassie Wright, assistant manager smiling at him. Not for the first time he gazed at her pretty, freckled face, her natural grin, those sparkling green eyes and cute, sexy cropped hair which emphasised her elegant neck. Whoever the boyfriend was, he was a lucky bastard. He went on the hotel's news tab and scanned through it. He chuckled to himself at seeing Adira, posing next to Jasper, from back when the Inn had opened their beauty treatment rooms and Adira had helped get them off the ground.

Then another thought came to him. He should go and visit her. He'd value her opinion on his work, plus he could really do with a good chat, to offload and talk about the current situation. Who better than Adira? He trusted her implicitly, and she knew the line of business he was in. She, more than anyone, would understand the strain he was under. The more he considered it, the better the idea became. The last time he was in Lilacwell, he had stayed on Adira and Jasper's glamping site, in a shep-herds hut, which had been great but looking at the Inn at Lilacwell, Rory decided he fancied a bit of luxury. Medi-cinal purposes, he told himself, recharging his batteries before the court case. Yes, that's the reason. Of course it was. He went back on the team page for another look at Cassie, then without any hesitation proceeded to book himself a room. Sorted. He was returning to Lilacwell.

Chapter 5

Cassie had just completed the staff rotas. After printing them out she made her way to reception, passing one of the housekeeping staff, who was just finishing a phone call.

'Hi, Lisa. Everything OK?'

'Yes thanks.' She gently patted her slightly rounded stomach.

'Starting to show now.' Cassie smiled at Lisa's action and the glow that had lit her eyes from the day she'd found out she was pregnant.

'I know!' she beamed.

'Take it easy though, won't you? Remember, no heavy lifting and more breaks.'

'Yes, don't worry, I'm being sensible,' confirmed Lisa. Too right she was – she and her husband had been desperate to start a family a few years ago, but it just wasn't happening. Then, when Adira had arrived in Lilacwell and made a name for herself with her natural herbal remedies, which had healed many an ailment, Lisa had decided to approach her. After all, thought Lisa, what had she to lose?

Now here she was, five months pregnant. Of course, Lisa knew it could have been a lot less straightforward, with fertility tests and goodness knows what else. But they had managed to succeed without such procedures, and for that she was thankful. Very thankful. Off the scale thankful, actually. She couldn't help but walk around with a smile permanently fixed on her face – so much so that Lisa's cheekbones ached (along with her back).

Cassie left Lisa to take another call and entered the reception room, which also doubled up as The Vintners, a gift shop selling wine that the hotel stocked as well as toiletries that the Inn used, and various other goods connected to shooting and fishing, which were popular activities in the area.

'Ah, Cassie, I just need to show our guests to their room,' said one of the staff from behind the reception desk.

'No problem, I'll man the fort,' she replied. Cassie busied herself tidying various bits of paperwork, then took a phone call for a booking. She opened the e-diary on the computer and completed the entries. On doing so, a name flashed before her, causing a sharp intake of breath. Rory Molloy. *Rory* was staying here? She leant forward and squinted her eyes. Opening them slowly confirmed that yes, he was. There, in black and white it read *Rory Molloy*, not once, but three times. He was staying three nights – Friday, Saturday and Sunday this week. Today was Wednesday, two days before he was due to arrive. Her heart started to thud in her chest. Why was Rory coming to Lilacwell and why was he staying at the Inn and not with Adira and Jasper? She pressed her lips and tried to concentrate on another guest wanting to buy wine.

'Which red would you recommend?' asked a lady pointing to the shelves lined with rows and rows of bottles.

The first one you see, thought Cassie, *and leave me in peace.*

'Err… the Chilean merlot is very popular,' she offered, all the time her mind was pedalling away, trying to take in what she'd just learnt.

Rory.

Here.

In. Two. Days.

'Right. Not the Argentinean malbec?'

Oh for pity's sake!

'Yes, yes that's also a good choice,' she nodded.

'What about the cabernet sauvignon from—'

'Yes, that too,' Cassie gave a bright smile.

'Oh, erm…'

Just pick one and go. Her eyes glanced back to the computer screen. Yes, he was still there, all three nights of him. Her heart began to pound again.

'Maybe I'll go for the…'

For the love of—

Turning her head she saw to her relief the member of staff return.

'Ah, could you help this lovely lady choose a bottle of red wine? I'm just needed elsewhere, thank you.' And off Cassie went before waiting for an answer.

She hurried up the stairs to her room and slammed the door shut. Steadying herself, she took deep breaths and tried to calm down.

'Don't overreact Cassie,' she said out loud. So what if Rory was staying at the hotel? It was no big deal. After all, they'd only spoken once, she told herself. *Yes, but what a connection*, whispered another voice inside.

What room was he in? She needed to get onto the booking system for his details. Tomorrow, she'd look tomorrow.

Ten minutes later, Cassie couldn't help but go back downstairs and into reception. Luckily it was empty. She quickly sat down and entered the password to get back into the e-diary. Clicking on his name told her he was in room twenty-one, the room opposite hers. Unbelievable. There was only one guest room on the top floor of the hotel, up in the eaves, and it would have to be that one. She imagined them both opening their doors in the morning, facing each other across the narrow corridor with awkward smiles. Even worse, what about night time, knowing they were sleeping literally yards away, both lying in bed practically mirroring each other? Cassie's chest started to pound again, a mixture of anxiety and excitement filling her. She couldn't deny her attraction to him, but she'd blown it, due to a panicked decision made in haste.

Then common sense kicked in. Did she really want another long-distance relationship? Those awful, cramped, monotonous train journeys sprung to mind. As did the London scene with Justin, forced to attend various events meeting other bankers. She had cringed at the brash way they had behaved; bellowing voices, loud guffaws, clicking fingers at waiters like they were the only ones in the room. They all had an air of upper-class superiority about them she hated. What had really upset her was the way Justin had joined in. He became one of them.

It hadn't always been like that, far from it, otherwise she'd never have struck up a relationship with him. Justin, too, had been a guest at the inn, part of a shooting party from down south who had checked in to enjoy the area renowned for its excellent grouse. Cassie had dropped a pile of menus when passing the party's table and Justin had been on his feet immediately to pick them up for her. Handing them back he'd grinned, looking boyish and carefree, which she had found rather endearing. His auburn hair was swept back and he had a faint, musky aroma of cedarwood. The paisley cravat she could forgive him, with manners like that. He was a gentleman.

'Oh thanks!' gushed Cassie blushing.

'My pleasure.' He didn't appear to be in any rush to return to his table, even though a few of his friends were throwing knowing looks. 'Justin Templeton, by the way.' He offered his hand out to shake.

'Cassie. Cassie Wright,' she'd replied a little flushed, balancing the menus with one hand, whilst freeing the other.

'Careful, don't drop them again,' he teased, his eyes never leaving her face. And the rest, was history. Justin had pursued her relentlessly and Cassie had been flattered. He was different from other boyfriends. He spoke eloquently, forever showering her with compliments. He was affluent and generous, giving her expensive presents – the heart-shaped diamond necklace he'd produced for her birthday was exquisite. Cassie appreciated how attentive Justin was. Yet, when he was with his work mates, he seemed to morph into a complete Hooray Henry. Their affectedly hearty voices and public-schoolboy antics rubbed off on him.

The final straw had been when one of them had slapped a young waitress's behind in a cocktail bar, sending the others, including Justin, into raucous laughter. Enough was enough, and it was at that precise point that Cassie had climbed down from the bar stool and stridden out. Justin hadn't even noticed she had left until twenty minutes later. Cassie had stuffed her belongings into an overnight bag and ordered a taxi to the railway station. She'd never looked back.

An inner voice prodded her, asking, was Rory like that? A human rights barrister, fighting for good causes?

That wretched twist tightened in her stomach. He certainly hadn't been surrounded by loud-mouthed, ineffectual toffs. Instead, the people Rory mixed with were trying to make a difference. They had morals. Never had she regretted such an ill, prejudiced judgement as the one she'd made at the summer party.

Chapter 6

The autumn days were creeping in, scattering vibrant colours over Lilacwell. There was a nip in the air and the faint smell of woodsmoke permeated the village. The nights grew darker as people hurried home to a warm, crackling fire.

Jasper threw back his whisky and narrowed his eyes in concentration. He was in the library, which he used as his study. He'd spent the day with his estate manager, Colin, and it had proved to be a productive one. At last, all the tenants' rents were bang up to date, with no arrears. The new glamping site, which had only been set up a few months ago, was making excellent progress, having been fully booked for the summer season, and the shepherds huts had been a tremendous success, along with the site where people could pitch their own tents. Everyone loved the great outdoors nowadays, or so it seemed; there definitely was an upward trend to holidaying at home, as opposed to travelling abroad, according to his books. Of course, now the summer peak had ended, the accounts would start to look very different out of season, but even so, Jasper remained optimistic. Especially when comparing the estate affairs before he'd returned from Dubai.

Jasper had had a wake-up call when seeing for himself just how run down The Laurels had been. Not to mention how lapse the estate business had been run. Now things were a whole lot different. Jasper, together with Adira, had whipped it all into shape, and a few months down the road were slowly beginning to see the fruits of their labour. He was proud of what they were achieving. He was proud of Adira; she had been a driving force behind him, always there to support and offer advice. As a trained barrister, she had easily tackled all the legalities in setting up the business, and she had creative flair, choosing the colours, fabrics and materials not only for the huts, but for The Laurels too. Together they had totally re-vamped the old, country house. Nobody was more grateful than Fletcher, who couldn't imagine life without them living there with him. 'It's just like the old days,' he'd say, reminiscing when The Laurels had played host to many a family occasion, bursting with love and laughter.

Now that The Laurels and the estate were in shape, Jasper and Adira could concentrate on the next big event – their wedding. At first, they had both thought of waiting till the following summer, but Jasper was starting to reconsider. He was a businessman with a close eye on the money. Looking at the accounts today told him the summer months counted, every single week of them. Having a wedding smack bang in the middle of this peak season could be financial suicide. The wedding would take up too much precious time, what with all the planning and preparation, plus accommodating all their guests with the shepherds huts, it would cost them thousands, literally. No, without wanting to appear too mercenary, he'd have to talk to Adira and persuade her to postpone. The last thing he wanted was all the hard work they'd both poured into the business to be in vain.

Adira was browsing through wedding magazines when Fletcher came into the kitchen. Smiling to himself he watched her engrossed, scanning each page closely, looking for inspiration.

'Found what you want yet, lass?' he asked cheerfully.

'Oh, hi Fletcher, sorry didn't see you there. No, not really, there's far too much choice.' That was an under-statement. It had been easier deciphering points of law as a barrister than deciding what dress, venue, guests, food, music, flowers and… theme? She looked again at the centre pages blazed with the headline, '*Theme or not to theme?*' What was that about? Adira laughed out loud at the pictures depicting some people's weddings – a Mad Hatter's Tea Party where all the guests were dressed in Alice in Wonderland characters; one couple had opted for a '*Great Gatsby*' wedding, dressed in gangster pinstriped suits and 1920's flapper dresses; another had gone for a WWII theme, which she found rather engaging, as the bride had worn her great-grandmother's wedding gown and the groom his great-grandfather's army uniform.

This had made Adira think about her relatives. Having researched her family history, she'd learnt that her great-great-grandmother was in fact buried in the churchyard at Lilacwell. It had transpired that when she'd stumbled upon Lilacwell, she had actually found the very roots of her family. For Adira this wasn't just a coincidence, it was pure fate. In her heart she knew she was meant to be here, in this special village.

'Well, you're going to have to make your mind up, lass,' said Fletcher, interrupting her thoughts. At this point Jasper joined them.

'It's no good, Jasper, I just can't decide on anything,' she said in frustration. Jasper closed the magazine and hugged her.

'Don't worry.' He kissed her hard on the mouth. 'We'll sit down and make plans tonight. Promise. I've gotta go.'

She frowned. 'Where are you going?'

'I'm going to look at a business unit.'

'Where?' said Fletcher and Adira simultaneously.

'Renovated farm buildings by Keepers Woods.'

Fletcher raised a brow. 'Oh, you mean Dickie Jenkins' farm?'

'You know it?' asked Jasper.

'Aye, I do that.'

An idea came to Jasper. 'Why don't you both come with me?'

'Good idea!' Fletcher claimed, glad to be included. Adira was just glad to take her mind off the wedding.

The three of them set off in the Land Rover, Jasper filling them in on the way with what he'd heard.

'It's a little complex of artisan shops by the river. It was previously a stable yard.'

'I remember them, old Dickie loved his horses,' said Fletcher, then added, 'So how come he's selling up?'

'His son's moved abroad and his grandson, Max, owns the forge there.'

'A forge?' Adira asked.

'Yes, apparently there's a forge, a carpentry studio, a pottery shop, florist and cafe.'

'How sweet! What's the place called?' she replied. Jasper's mouth twitched slightly, knowing full well what her reaction would be.

'The Cobbled Courtyard.'

'Oh, how lovely!' Her face lit up with enthusiasm.

'So you're thinking of buying the complex off old Dickie?' Fletcher was looking thoughtful.

'Yes, but keeping the status quo, renting the units to the same people, at the same cost.'

'But why doesn't Max take over from him?' Fletcher was a stickler for keeping property in the family, especially farms. In his eyes that was a must, passing down from father to son.

'Max is too busy with his forge. I suspect he's getting a cut from the sale.'

'But can you afford it? We've only just started our business.' Adira eyed him carefully. Did he look a tad uncomfortable?

'We can... if—'

'If what?' she interrupted, suddenly becoming wary.

Jasper sighed. 'If we don't have a big summer wedding.' A short silence followed. Shit. He'd anticipated saying all this tonight. Not in the car with Fletcher listening. 'Looking at the accounts this morning made me realise just how much the cost and the timing will affect us. We've really got to make the summer months count, Adira, pack as many people in as possible. Having a wedding in the middle of it all will wipe out precious income.'

'Oh, right.'

He put his hand on her lap. 'You do see, don't you? If we postpone the wedding, the cash projection would mean we could expand the business.'

'And buy The Cobbled Courtyard?'

'Yes,' he nodded.

Adira sat back in her seat and considered it all. Did she really want a big summer wedding anyway? Trawling through those magazines had been a nightmare, in all honesty. She glanced sideways at Jasper, his face set in determination. He really wanted this business opportunity, she could tell. A simple classy ceremony, without any fuss and bother rather appealed to her. She pictured them holding hands, exchanging vows in The Laurels' orangery, surrounded by just immediate family, and she relaxed. That tense, tightening feeling in her chest eased up. A hassle-free wedding. She liked the sound of that.

'I don't think we should postpone the wedding,' she said. Jasper's shoulders dropped. 'Let's get married as soon as possible, a nice quiet affair.'

He turned to face her and couldn't help the grin that spread across his face. 'You sure?'

'Yes. Let's do it.'

'Good. That's settled then,' Fletcher cheered from the back seat.

Chapter 7

Rory was packing his case, looking forward to a mini-break. He'd emailed Adira and told her he was visiting Lilacwell. She'd offered to accommodate him, but when he'd explained he was staying at the inn, her jaunty reply of '*Of course you are!*' made him smile wryly to himself. Later on reflection, it made him think. Did that jovial remark really mean 'of course you are, because you fancy seeing Cassie' or was it simply a casual remark on him wanting a little luxury? Then, with his barrister's interrogation head on, if it was the first, wouldn't that be slightly inappropriate, given Cassie was in a relationship? Adira wasn't the sort to want to come between a couple. Perhaps he was overthinking it. In any event, he intended to enjoy a few days of peace and tranquillity in the country, away from all the attention the protesters were attracting.

Luckily, he had completed all the other cases which he'd been working on, leaving him with just them to concentrate on. He half thought that it had been a deliberate move by Nigel Kerfoot, not to allocate him any more briefs. It was exactly the kind of instruction he would give; the sneaky swine was hedging his bets. The activists' case could either be a rip-roaring success, putting his chambers in a glorious light, or an unmitigated disaster, dragging them all down by association. Leaving Rory without any continuing briefs meant he could be disposed of quickly, if need be. Rory could read him like a book. He was aware of how other barristers had been treated by the Head before, often unfairly. Equally, those in favour would receive the 'Nigel perks', such as dinners at The Ivy, or tickets for a West End play. Of course, they usually involved the more attractive ladies, or those in the old boys' network, of which Rory was most decidedly not a member.

The more Rory considered his working environment, the more he questioned it. True, his barrister's salary had provided well, giving him his comfortable apartment in a leafy north London quarter. He drove an Audi TT Convertible which he hoped didn't appear too flash, but was unable to resist buying at the time. His parents had been so proud when he first got his position at Goldgate Chambers. They still were, especially when seeing their son on the news, fighting for a good cause. Rory had been born into a working-class family and had had a modest but happy upbringing. He was the youngest of three boys and the brightest by far. His father made sure his cleverest son received the best possible education and had sent him to the local grammar school in Lancaster. Here, Rory had flourished and gone on to graduate at Lancaster University with a first in law, going from strength to strength until finally moving to London.

Initially, Rory had hated the capital. It was a far cry from the historical city of Lancaster where he called home. It was far too busy, noisy, dirty and expensive. It was unfriendly, with everybody dashing about the place in a hurry. He appreciated the museums, and that was about it. Most weekends he'd travel back up north, but as work increased and took over, Rory had to spend all his spare time buried in law books and paperwork.

He'd had two relationships since moving to London. The first was a girl from the north too, which made a refreshing change, but she'd planned to go backpacking for a year, putting an end to things. Then there'd been Sonya, not his usual type, being a leggy blonde with a posh drawl, but she'd struck him as quite down to earth, despite her middle-class background. It was never destined to be a long-term affair, especially given the way her mother had doomed him from the start. His Lancashire accent hadn't cut the mustard, however his job did, so he was granted some reprieve. After a rather disastrous family meal, 'a simple kitchen supper, nothing too elaborate', he admitted defeat and called it a day; apparently passing bread rolls the wrong way and drinking out of the wrong glass proved too much for her mother, in the same way her 'elbows *off* the table, Rory', proved too much for him.

He was single and lonely in London, so it hadn't surprised Rory that after a trip back home, he'd met someone who he thought was just right. Miss Wright. The way they'd connected was seamless, each making the other laugh, both interested in what they had to say. He definitely got the impression she was attracted to him, not that he was overconfident, but her demeanour spoke volumes, the way she was discreetly sizing him up. Rory was used to female attention, he knew the signs and Cassie was most certainly giving them. Until he mentioned where he lived; then it all came to an abrupt holt and bang, the door was firmly shut. Her body language became rigid and all eye contact ceased. He'd been staggered and tried hard not to show his disappointment when she'd suddenly decided to mention her boyfriend. Up until then she'd given no hint of one. The change in her behaviour had been too extreme and it had been a bit of an enigma – one he was determined to solve.

–

It was Friday. Cassie knew that instantly on waking, because a tingly anticipation filled her. Today was *the* day. Rory was arriving at the hotel. Cool, calm and professional – that was her mantra, yet inside she felt anything but. In her head she'd built it up too much and now she needed to settle her nerves. It was just a case of putting things in perspective, that's what she kept telling herself.

Cassie had tried to get hold of Adira over the past few days, but her friend had been too busy with Jasper. She'd promised to catch up soon, but things were too hectic at the moment. Cassie had sensed a slightly secretive tone to Adira's voice, like she was hiding something. She'd so desperately wanted to ask her about Rory staying but hadn't been given the chance and, as a result, she was still clueless as to why he was visiting.

As weekends go, it was going to be a busy one. The Inn was completely booked and Cassie was glad of the distraction; she wanted to be as preoccupied as possible. She'd noticed that Rory had booked in for dinner each night. They'd put him in the secluded alcove by the inglenook fire, knowing that most people dining alone didn't like to be on show in the middle of the room.

They'd had barristers from London staying at the Inn before, working on High Court cases in Preston, but something told Cassie that Rory wasn't coming there for business. He was currently representing the climate protesters in Goldgate, so it was unlikely he'd be needed up north. Cassie was more than curious.

As she went downstairs, her eyes did the usual sweep of the building, making sure all was well, clean and tidy. Breakfasts were being served and there was a hub of activity. Soon, the dining area would be empty and the staff would then clear the tables for lunch.

Cassie was busy on her feet all morning and by the time late afternoon rolled around, all the hotel guests had checked in, apart from Rory. Every so often she'd peek out of a window looking onto the car park at the front, to see if there was any sign of him. She was in reception when her phone bleeped with a text message from Adira.

> Hi, free tonight? Guess who's staying with you?

Cassie shook her head. Typical. Why couldn't she have texted before today? Still, it would be nice to finally catch up with her and it was her night off.

> Yes, free tonight. Shall I come to yours?

Immediately her phone pinged back with a reply, which she was just about to read, when a cough made her suddenly look up. It was Rory. There he was, standing tall and handsome, looking at her. He was wearing black jeans and a fitted, black leather jacket, outlining his broad shoulders. His dark curls fell into his eyes and he swept them back, reminding her of how he'd looked on TV. He had a small suitcase beside him.

'Hello, Cassie,' he smiled.

'H–hi.' Was that squeaky voice really hers?

There was a pause.

'I need to check in?' he said with a grin.

'Oh, err... yes of course, sorry.' With slightly shaking hands, Cassie reached for the room key and a visitor's sheet which he needed to complete. 'There you go. Room twenty-one. Could you fill this in please?' She passed him the key, his fingers touching hers, then placed the sheet of paper in front of him on the desk. He pulled a pen out of his pocket – silver and expensive looking – and began completing his details. Cassie's eyes cast over his writing: bold, clear strokes. She clocked his address: 10 Hollins House, Lowther Gardens, North London. It sounded rather swanky to her. He gave his car registration – it wasn't a personal one, which somehow pleased her – then his mobile number. All done. He smiled and gave her the sheet back. 'Thanks,' she replied. 'Right, I'll show you to your room.' He stood back and let her lead the way.

He followed her through the hall to the stairs, all the time assessing her shapely legs, slim build, elegant neck and that snappy, pixie-cut hair he found extremely sexy. Only once did she turn, a touch self-consciously he thought, to make sure he was keeping up. Soon they had reached the second floor.

'Here we are, right at the top, up in the eaves,' she said brightly.

'Lovely, thanks.' He looked at her for a moment. 'I'm impressed. You're not even out of breath.'

'Oh, I'm used to the stairs, that's my room,' she pointed to the door opposite his, then instantly faltered. Did she really just say that? She blushed furiously. Rory's eyes swept over to her door, then rested on her. Was he hiding a smirk?

'Really?'

'Err… yes,' she stumbled, not knowing what to say.

'I know where to come for a nightcap then,' he replied with a cheeky wink. She couldn't help but giggle. Somehow it broke the ice a little and she relaxed.

'Sorry, was that a touch unprofessional of me?' she asked, still half laughing. He shook his head with a wide, genuine smile.

'Be as unprofessional as you like.'

Was he teasing her?

'Anyway, hope everything's to your liking,' Cassie tried to switch back to managerial mode.

'So far, so good,' he replied, with a pointed look.

Was he flirting with her?

'Right, I'll let you get on.'

'OK, thanks Cassie,' he turned to put the key in the lock.

Cassie couldn't help but smile to herself walking back down the stairs. Then she remembered to open Adira's text message.

I'll come to you. I want to see Rory too.

Cassie quickly rang back. She so needed to speak to her before she saw Rory, but Adira didn't pick up.

–

Rory closed his door and weighed up the room. He took in the four-poster bed, antique furniture, velvet drapes and huge sash window giving panoramic views of the stunning landscape. He was at the rear of the house, which over-looked the river and terrace garden. It really was special

38

and he could see why the hotel and area had such a good reputation. His own apartment was tasteful enough and had pleasant views of a communal garden, but this was something else. He went to inspect the bathroom and was equally impressed, all black marble with a roll-top bath and spotlights. Very sleek, he thought. Then his mind wandered to across the landing and what Cassie's room was like. Cassie. Hell, she intrigued him. He was convinced his first instincts had been right, there was undeniably chemistry between them. Then his thoughts turned to her boyfriend. What was *he* like? Maybe he'd see him. Was he even still on the scene? He'd found it easy to tease her. She clearly had a sense of humour and they both seemed to be on the same wavelength. Exactly as it had been when first meeting.

He decided to have a good soak in that roll-top bath and rest, feeling tired from the journey and needing to unwind. As he lay there amongst the bubbles, his eyes closed and he enjoyed the quiet, the burdens he carried from London seeming to rise from his shoulders along with the steam from the water.

Later in the evening he entered the bar and ordered a beer before being seated at his table. He once again observed his surroundings. How quaint it was, he thought, with its stone floors, open fires, old oak tables, mismatched chairs, and pictures of the local area on the walls. No intrusive music here, just the gentle sound of chat and laughter. The place oozed country charm, where dogs lay quietly by either muddy boots or polished brogues. The clientele was a mixture of young, old and families, from smartly dressed couples to jovial farmers throwing back their pints. Rory warmed to it, liking the homely atmosphere the Inn had created.

After a delicious meal of steak and ale pie, he ordered another drink and waited for Adira to arrive. She'd messaged him to say she'd be there later and he was looking forward to seeing her, and seeking her advice. He was ever mindful the court hearing would soon be upon him and he was increasingly desperate to pick her brains over it. Then he saw her enter the bar. He waved until she spotted him, weaving her way through the tables to sit opposite him.

'Hi!' she beamed.

Rory stood up to kiss her cheek. 'Hello you. How's tricks?'

'Never better and you? Making quite a name for yourself I see,' she grinned. He rolled his eyes.

'I know. But it's not about me, it's about bringing attention to—'

'I know, I know, the climate crisis,' she softly interrupted, then sat back to examine him. 'How's the chambers taking it, you representing a bunch of activists?'

He shrugged. 'Don't care.'

'Rory Molloy, the maverick,' she chuckled.

'Actually, I was going to ask a favour,' he said, leaning forward. 'Could I run a few points of law past you? See what you think?'

'Yes, of course,' Adira replied in surprise. 'For a minute, I thought you were going to ask me to put in a good word for you.'

'Sorry?'

'With Cassie?' she playfully raised her eyebrow.

'Not sure her boyfriend would appreciate that,' he said, just as he noticed Cassie herself approaching them.

'What boyfriend?' Adira asked, before they both turned to face her.

Chapter 8

The next day, as promised, Adira was studying Rory's notes on the activists' case. From what she saw, he'd covered just about everything. Not that she'd been expecting to see any holes in his defence. Rory was known for his attention to detail, which was why he was highly sought after. He really was a credit to Goldgate Chambers. Her only concern was how this case would leave him. She, more than most, knew how cut-throat that line of business could be, which was exactly why she had chosen to cut and run. Adira had never regretted it for a moment.

She was in the library, sat at Jasper's desk, when in he came.

'Ah, there you are.' He sank into a nearby sofa.

'I'm just looking at Rory's defence. He thinks that court proceedings will be imminent.'

'Right.' He looked closely at her, then added, 'Have you thought any more about the wedding?'

'I've thought of little else,' she said, turning to him. 'Jasper, I'm thinking of applying for a licence, to hold ceremonies here, at The Laurels.'

He frowned in thought. 'Where?'

'In the orangery.' She went to sit next to him, twisting her body to face his and tucking her legs beneath her. 'Just think, it would be beautiful, all decorated with flowers and candles. It's the perfect size for an intimate wedding like ours.'

'I see,' he nodded, liking the sound of it.

Hearing the interest in his tone, Adira continued with enthusiasm, 'It would make a fantastic venue for the business, all guests staying on the glamping site.'

'Yes, it would.' Jasper's mind was ticking over.

'We could make a wedding package, really go to town.'

'I like your thinking.' He smiled, reaching out to tuck a strand of hair behind her ear, then added, 'How soon could we get a licence?'

'Not too long. I've already made some enquires.' Jasper laughed. A girl after his own heart.

'Go for it. I think it's a fantastic idea.'

Adira was glad of his approval, then as an afterthought asked, 'Do you think Fletcher would mind?'

'You kidding? He'd love it, the place full of people partying.' Wrapping an arm round her body, he pulled her to him. He kissed her neck, then slowly moved upwards towards her mouth. Adira turned to meet his lips, warm and inviting, probing hers. Her hands ran across his broad shoulders then to his silky dark hair. That familiar fragrance of bergamot hit her, along with a wave of desire. Jasper deepened the kiss, moving further into her.

'Jasper...' she whimpered. Just then, Fletcher barged in. The two hastily separated, slightly out of breath.

'I've been thinking,' he announced, totally oblivious to what he'd walked in on, 'about that there Cobbled... whatever.'

'Courtyard,' supplied Jasper.

'Yes. Dickie's buildings. I want you to put in the asking price.'

'But why?' asked Adira. 'Surely nobody does that, do they?'

'Round here, amongst good, honest farmers, yes, they do.' He faced Adira with conviction.

'Won't he be expecting some negotiation?' Jasper frowned.

'Is he asking a fair price?' Fletcher asked.

'Yes, actually, I think he is,' conceded Jasper.

'Well then, don't insult the man by offering less.' Fletcher nodded his head firmly.

Jasper was inclined to agree. He knew how things operated in the country, where everyone knew each other. He understood why Fletcher wouldn't want to offend a neighbour he'd always known.

'OK then. I'll offer the asking price.'

Fletcher stared at him expectantly. 'Well go on then.' He pointed to the phone on his desk.

'What, now?'

'Yes, yes, what are you waiting for?' he answered impatiently, making Adira hide a smile.

'You sure about this, Fletcher?' Jasper asked, before moving off the sofa to pick up the phone.

'Yes. Get on with it, man.'

After several minutes of conversation with the estate agents, Jasper put the receiver down. 'They'll get back to me as soon as possible,' he confirmed.

'Oh blow that. I'm ringing Dickie meself,' Fletcher exclaimed in exasperation.

'You can't do that, Fletcher,' laughed Adira.

'Watch me,' and with that strode over to the book-case and pulled out an address book. Taking it, he put it down in front of Jasper sat at the desk. 'Just read me the number of Jenkins' farm. It's in there somewhere.'

Somewhat bemused, Jasper dutifully did as he was told. After a few moments, Fletcher spoke. 'That you, Dickie? It's Fletcher here. About your old stables, we want them.' There was a slight pause. 'Aye, we'll give you what you want.' Another pause. 'You'll take 'em off the market then?' swiftly followed by, 'Good, good. Bye.' Then down went the phone. He turned to face them both. 'Right, they're ours.' Then strode out of the room with purpose, leaving Jasper and Adira speechless.

Honestly, thought Fletcher, if only everyone took the bull by the horns and got on with it like he did. Lilly, she was another, fussing and faffing about. Why she couldn't just say yes to his suggestion of a holiday was beyond him. He made his way into the kitchen to find her ironing whilst humming along to the radio.

'Would you like a coffee, Fletcher?' she asked, looking up.

'No thanks, Lilly. I'd like an answer though, about this 'ere river cruise.'

'Oh, that again,' she replied, her face slightly falling.

'What is it lass? Why are you stalling?' he asked.

'I do want to go... it's just...'

'What?'

'Ruby. I don't want to leave Ruby.'

Fletcher closed his eyes. Of course, why hadn't he thought of that? Ruby was her twin sister; they'd always lived together. It was only natural that Lilly wouldn't want to leave her behind.

'But it's only for a few days, Lilly,' Fletcher tried to reason.

'I know, but it still wouldn't feel right, me leaving her to swan off on a cruise when she'd still be at home, all alone.'

Fletcher considered this, a sadness coming over him. Whilst he understood Lilly's dilemma, he couldn't help but feel remorse at what she was sacrificing. He didn't like the thought of going alone either. The idea of him sailing off solo really didn't appeal. So, with that in mind, he took a deep breath and prayed he wouldn't live to regret what he was about to propose.

'Right then, how about Ruby coming too?'

Lilly's face shot up in delight. 'Really? Do you mean that?'

'Aye, if that's what it takes.'

'Oh, Fletcher! Thank you so much.'

Cassie was driving back to the hotel. It was her day off and she'd spent the morning in the nearby town of Clitheroe, enjoying a little retail therapy. She'd also made an impromptu visit to the hairdresser's and had a few golden highlights put into her chestnut hair. Feeling upbeat, she sang in tune to the song on the radio.

As she drove along the country lane leading to the inn, she saw a figure jogging in the distance. Getting nearer, she realised it was Rory, recognising those dark curls and tall, solid frame in shorts and T-shirt. Slowing down, her eyes homed in on his powerful legs pounding the ground. He turned on hearing her car and waved. She wound down her window.

'Do you want a lift back?' she called. He shook his head.

'No thanks. Gotta finish.' Then he gave her the thumbs up.

'OK, bye!'

Cassie continued on, glancing in the rear-view mirror. She watched him run effortlessly up the incline. What a powerhouse he was. A hot surge glowed through her.

Last night she'd caught the tail end of his and Adira's conversation. Basically, Adira had inadvertently dropped her in it, but Rory, very gallantly, chose not to take issue and had let Adira's remark pass. Getting up from the table, he had asked them both what they were drinking and headed for the bar, leaving Adira and Cassie alone.

'Why did you tell Rory you had a boyfriend?' she'd hissed.

Cassie had let out a huge sigh.

'Sorry, I just got cold feet,' she replied lamely.

'Why? Rory's a great guy.' Adira sounded almost incredulous.

'I-I… thought because he lived in London—'

'It'd be like dating Justin?' Adira cut in sharply. Cassie weakly nodded her head. 'Listen, Rory is *nothing* like Justin, believe me,' she blazed under her breath. It was the first time Cassie had ever seen Adira look so cross.

'I know, sorry,' she gulped, then quickly sat back and tried to look casual on seeing him return.

The rest of the evening had passed pleasantly, despite the rocky start. Adira had told them excitedly about her forthcoming wedding, now brought forward to Christmas. Cassie's eyes had widened, knowing how much work would be involved to organise the event.

'How will you manage it? You've less than three months?' she'd squealed.

'It's in hand,' Adira had reassured smoothly. 'It's just going to be a small, intimate affair.'

'Am I invited then?' asked Rory with a grin.

'Of course, and you can bring her, if you want,' she joked, pointing at Cassie. At this Rory had turned to look her full in the face. His blue eyes bored into hers.

'I just might,' he said quietly, making Cassie's insides melt. Good God, he was handsome.

The three of them had chatted all night. Rory had briefly talked about the Goldgate activists. Whilst Adira had listened, asking all the right questions, Cassie had sat in awe. His passion was evident, as was his intellect. He spoke animatedly, every now and then pushing back his hair from his face. He reminded Cassie of a swarthy *Poldark* figure, all masculine, fighting for the good, and she could well imagine him in court, eloquently making his case. What had made the biggest impact on her opinion of him though, was learning he was acting free of charge. Undoubtedly Adira had been right, Rory was the polar opposite to the likes of Justin. Cassie couldn't help but stare at him, when suddenly she became conscious of Adira gently kicking her foot under the table, giving her a knowing smile. Adira knew full well she'd been lusting after him and wasn't going to let it pass.

After driving back to the inn, later in the afternoon, she'd called in at The Laurels. Adira answered the front door with a Cheshire cat smile, making Cassie laugh.

'I've been a complete fool,' she quickly claimed before giving Adira chance to scold her.

'Correct. Come in.'

Adira made them both a coffee and they sat at the breakfast bar. 'Cassie, I meant what I said. Rory really is nothing like Justin.'

'I know,' she exhaled, 'but he does live in London and I really don't want another long-distance relationship.'

'It's only a couple of hours' train ride, Cass.'

'Yeah, but it's not just that, it's getting the time to travel. With my job it's hard and it would just be snatched odd days.' Adira listened, seeing her friend's point, even though she thought they made a good couple. Adira knew from experience that Rory's career wouldn't allow him much free time to travel either. Cassie continued, 'I do love my job, but sometimes I feel married to it, living and working at the inn. It can be so binding.'

Adira nodded, understanding her predicament. 'Don't you think it's worth having this conversation with him?' she gently asked.

'What's the point?' Cassie sounded so defeated.

'Oh come on, Cass, you couldn't take your eyes of him,' Adira chuckled. 'There's got to be a way round it.' If she knew Rory, then there definitely would be. She'd seen him fight for what he wanted. He was persistent, relentless and fearless in his actions. Once he set his heart on something, he wouldn't let go, of that Adira was certain. And she was pretty certain Rory wanted Cassie.

Chapter 9

Rory lay soaking in the bath again. He'd earned it, rising early to look at the emails stacking up on his laptop, answering a few calls and then going for a five-mile run late morning. He'd taken a drive round the area, loving the country roads where he could put his foot down, hugging the bends and accelerating on the open stretches; a far cry from sitting in the London traffic. It had been cold but dry, so he'd driven with his roof down letting the wind exhilarate him. Breathing in the fresh, clean air, he realised just how much he missed being up north. It was his second day in Lilacwell and already he felt an affinity to the place. He fully appreciated why Adira had chosen to stay here.

Having parked on the village church car park, he'd walked down into the little high street, visiting a coffee shop, and later roamed through the various artisan shops. He couldn't remember the last time he'd done something so relaxing, just slowing down and taking time to value his surroundings. Small things like hearing birdsong as he woke, the trickle of a stream, owls hooting at night, the chug of a tractor, the cry of a cockerel, all country sounds that resonated with him. He'd always resented the roar of traffic, tooting horns and sirens that constantly echoed around London. The thought of a future living there filled him with dread. The money was good, but that wasn't enough, he was beginning to learn. Having time out like today had taught him that. Rory wasn't materialistic, he'd simply been drawn onto the treadmill of city life. It was only when he'd stepped off for a moment that he could see what he actually wanted, what would make him happy. Without realising it, he had been operating on autopilot – work, sleep, then work again. As he'd driven back through the leafy lanes, admiring the rolling hills, verdant forests and waterfalls, he'd longed to stay. A tinge of sadness stung him at the thought of leaving.

Adira had rung him to say she'd been impressed with what she had read, which had given him some much-needed confidence. It was good to have a second opinion and he valued Adira's. She'd also mischievously hinted that Cassie was free that evening.

'Is she really?' he'd replied in good humour.

'Hmm, I think you two should talk,' she replied, her voice taking a serious tone.

'Yes. We should.' He sounded rather determined, which is exactly what Adira had expected. There, she'd done her bit, the rest was down to them.

That evening when he came down for dinner, he couldn't see Cassie, so ordered a pint and went straight to his table. Within a few minutes she was walking past.

She stopped and smiled. 'Hi, good day?'

'Yes, thanks,' he replied looking directly at her, some-what accusingly.

'Everything all right?' She frowned.

'No.'

'Oh.' Cassie's face fell. 'Anything I can help with?'

'Yes. You can sit down and tell me why you lied about having a boyfriend.' His eyes were piercing into her. She swallowed, thinking how good he must be cross-examining in court. Cassie sat down.

'Rory, I'm sorry—'

'I don't want an apology, just an explanation.' He took a drink, all the time his eyes never leaving her face.

'Yes, OK.' Cassie's voice quivered slightly. 'I've previously had a long-distance relationship and… it didn't work. I hated all the travelling—'

'Did he not come here?' interrupted Rory softly. He hated seeing her so vulnerable and hearing the shake in her voice.

Cassie shook her head. 'Not much.'

'Why?'

'Well… he was always too busy…'

'What did he do?'

'He was a banker.'

'Sounds it,' he muttered under his breath. 'So, basically he didn't make the effort and expected you to do all the running?'

There was a pregnant pause. Cassie was taken aback by his frankness.

'I went to London more than he came here, yes.'

Rory tilted his head to one side. 'I see, so as soon as I mentioned living in London, the barriers came up.'

Cassie swallowed again. 'Yes,' she whispered in a small voice, then looked down.

Rory, seeing her so vulnerable, put his hand over hers. Her head jerked up to look at him. Did she have tears in her eyes?

'Cassie,' he spoke softly, 'don't shut me out.' He leant forward and kissed her lips. It was a fleeting kiss, but loaded, taking her breath away. He sat back and their eyes met. Cassie gave a shy, knowing smile. Was this a signal? 'Stay and have dinner with me.'

Cassie's smile widened, 'Yes, I'd like that.'

Time flew as the pair of them chatted and laughed in the cosy alcove by the fire. Cassie told him about her family and how she'd always loved living in Lilacwell. Rory had spoken of his childhood, too, in Lancaster.

'Don't you miss the north?' asked Cassie, finishing her glass of wine.

'Terribly,' he'd replied, pouring them both another. They were both feeling nicely relaxed from the wine, the warmth of the room, and the effortless flow of conversation.

'Do you think you'll ever come back?' She watched his face closely. His jaw tightened.

'I dearly hope so.' He took a sip of wine and gazed straight at her, making Cassie's heart pound. Their eyes locked, no words necessary. Then, after a moment Rory asked, 'How about that night cap?'

Together they made their way up the stairs. Cassie opened her door and Rory followed her in. Her room was very spacious, with a split-level floor leading from the living area on the top down a step to the bedroom.

'Very nice,' Rory commented, looking round. It was decorated in the same style as his room with antique furniture and heavy curtains to keep out the cold.

'Thanks. Will gin do? Or should I order coffee?'

'Gin's fine, thanks.'

She poured the drinks from a cabinet then came and sat next to him with two large glasses.

'This is a lovely place to live.' Rory turned to her and took his drink.

'It is, but it can be quite suffocating at times, living and working in the same place. You're always on call.'

'Do you think you'll ever leave?' Rory echoed her question to him from earlier, examining her reaction carefully.

'I'd really like to be my own boss.'

'You mean own your own hotel?'

'My own business. Not necessarily hotel.' She took a long gulp of her gin and tonic. 'I like the idea of being my own boss.'

Rory nodded, knowing exactly what she meant. Hadn't he been having similar thoughts? They really were alike, kindred spirits in so many ways. He put his glass down and stretched out his arm for her to snuggle up to him.

'Come here, Pixie.'

'Pixie?' she giggled, cosying up to him. His gorgeous citrus spice fragrance intoxicated her senses.

'Yes, from the moment I saw you, I loved this sexy little number.' He toyed with the ends of her hair, his fingertips brushing against the back of her neck, sending shivers down her spine. 'What have you done to it? It looks different.'

'Had it highlighted,' she said, glad he'd noticed. Then she felt him kiss the top of her head. She looked up into his eyes. Instinctively, their bodies moved towards each other, mouths meeting halfway. Rory's hands cupped her face as his tongue ran across her lower lip, making her quiver in delight. Her heart was thumping again, as the kiss became more intense. Cassie reached up to run her fingers through his curls. He groaned and pulled her closer, trailing kisses down her neck and collarbone. Cassie's hands found the inside of his shirt and ran across his taut back and shoulders, loving the firm, muscular contours of his body.

'Cassie,' he moaned, as his mouth found hers once more. He so wanted to pick up her beautiful body and devour her on the bed yards away from them. But he couldn't. It was too soon. With superhuman effort, he brought the kiss to a halt, his chest heaving.

'You OK, Rory?' she whispered looking concerned.

'Sorry, Cassie.' He touched her cheek. 'I don't want to rush things.' He searched her face, hoping she understood and felt the same way.

She took his hand and held it. 'It's fine, don't worry.'

'We'll spend tomorrow together?' he asked.

'Yes. I'll get cover.' She'd manage it, somehow. It was his last day.

'Good night.' He kissed her again, then stood up.

'Good night.' She joined him and saw him out onto the corridor. Closing her door, she couldn't help but punch the air.

Chapter 10

Jasper and Adira were walking hand in hand through Keepers Woods. It felt good to be at one with nature together. All the hustle and bustle of running a new business, organising a wedding and buying The Cobbled Courtyard were beginning to take their toll. Jasper was looking tired and weary. Adira was slightly worried about him, but was told, 'I'm fine,' every time she voiced her concerns. It had been her idea to stroll through the forest on their way to The Cobbled Courtyard instead of driving. They were about to have a good look around again and Max, Dickie's grandson, was going to introduce them to their new tenants. Jasper was keen to familiarise himself and didn't want to waste any time, even though the sale hadn't been officially completed.

As they strolled through the verdant woodland along the limestone path, wood pigeons called in the distance. The smell of wild garlic and damp earth filled the air. Dappled sunlight glowed through the branches. As they reached the outskirts of the forest, they passed a cute, wooden house nestled in the trees. The sign outside told them it was 'Woodsman Cottage'.

'Oh, look, how adorable!' exclaimed Adira, pointing to it.

'I know, apparently it belongs to one of the tenants,' said Jasper.

'Which one?'

'The guy who owns Crafty Carpentry.'

'Ah, that figures. What a craftsman he must be.' She admired the arched windows, oak door with large cast-iron hinges, low slated roof with stove flue poking out, puffing smoke, and a decked veranda where an empty hammock gently rocked in the breeze.

'They all are, in their own right, I'm guessing.'

'How do you think they'll react to us?' Adira hoped they weren't upsetting the applecart.

'I think they'll be glad the new owners are local.'

Yes, that's what they were now – locals. The thought gave Adira a warm, reassuring feeling. The fact that Dickie and Fletcher were old acquaintances would be a comfort to the tenants, too, no doubt. She was beginning to comprehend the way things functioned in the country. She still chuckled when picturing how Fletcher had dealt with buying The Cobbled Courtyard, in his own inimitable style. In her quieter moments, she contemplated how good a grandfather figure he would make to their future children and, when doing so, Adira observed how the thought of motherhood wasn't a daunting one, which it had been up until now. Instead, she found herself imagining what her offspring would look like. Dark and swarthy like Jasper, or pale and blonde like her?

'What's going on through that mind of yours, Miss Summers?' Jasper squeezed her hand, seeing her deep in concentration.

'Just glad I'm here with you,' she smiled and kissed his cheek.

Max was ready and waiting for them as they entered the small courtyard. It struck Adira again just how pretty the place was with its quaint set of craft shops, each with a brightly coloured wooden door and their own sign depicting what each unit was. The pottery studio was called The Potter's Bolthole, the florist's, Fresh Bouquet, and had a flower box bursting with orange and yellow dahlias and cream chrysanthemums. The Hot Spot was Max's forge and the workshop, Crafty Carpentry, had a wooden carved statue of a Green Man stood solemnly at the door. Finally, there was the Courtyard Cafe which looked warm and welcoming with its pastel coloured bunting, swooping across the outdoor decking area with bistro sets.

'Hello, Jasper.' Max held out a dusty charcoaled hand. His face, too, was smeared with black dust, as were his overalls, but that didn't prevent Jasper from shaking his hand.

'Hi, Max, this is my fiancée, Adira.'

'Hi,' he nodded in her direction.

'Hello, Max, lovely to meet you.'

'Come on, let's meet everyone. We're a friendly bunch,' he smiled. He led them to the carpentry workshop first, where a man wearing protective goggles was sanding down wood. He turned off the sander and took off his goggles when seeing them enter. 'Meet the new owners, Jasper and Adira,' said Max, then turned to them. 'This is Fitz.' They all shook hands.

'Is that your gorgeous little cottage in the woods?' Adira asked.

'Yes,' he smiled, 'it is.'

'Did you build it?' she replied.

'I did.'

'Oh, it's amazing!' Max and Jasper exchanged grins. Jasper guessed this was a reaction that Fitz was used to. He seemed pretty modest though in accepting Adira's praises.

'How long have you been here?' Jasper asked.

'Not long actually. Just under two years.'

'Fitz is the newest tenant,' added Max. 'The rest have been here ages. Jessie, the potter, will be retiring, so her unit will be free in a few months.'

'Right, I see,' replied Jasper, thinking ahead. He'd need to get it advertised as soon as she gave notice.

'I'll introduce you to the rest,' Max said before guiding them into each unit.

Jessie was a lovely old lady and a hugely talented potter, judging by the ceramics displayed on the shelves. James, who ran the florist's, was an impeccably dressed middle-aged man and softly spoken. Lastly, Max took them to the cafe, where they met Tom and Tess, the young couple who managed it. Adira loved the decor, all distressed wooden panelling and pastel fittings. It always astounded her how proficient people were at working the large silver coffee machines with various levers and buttons, hissing out steam.

'Sit down, I'll get the drinks in,' said Jasper.

'Thanks,' replied Max. 'I'll have my usual, Tom,' he called over the counter.

Jasper was extremely pleased with what he'd seen. He also had a good feeling about the tenants. They all seemed decent people he could do business with, especially Max. That said, a part of him couldn't help but sense a touch of guilt at buying what was his inheritance. After chatting over coffee, he decided to broach the subject.

'Max, can I ask why you don't want to take over the business?'

'I'm happy doing what I do best, being a blacksmith,' he shrugged, not looking in the least offended by the question. 'Granddad is making sure I get my share, so no one's missing out.'

'Good,' Jasper nodded, his conscience appeased. Adira looked thoughtfully on. Max was obviously a practical, hands-on man who loved his craft. She didn't envisage him in a suit, pen pushing, sorting out the book work and tax returns. Why should he? Each to their own, was her mentality. Look at what she'd done – quit her career as a barrister to run a glamping site in the sticks – and she'd never been happier.

She and Jasper walked home in quiet contemplation, each knowing that buying The Cobbled Courtyard was the right move.

Chapter 11

Cassie saw the note pushed under her door and read it with a wide smile.

> Morning Pixie,
>   Meet me at 10 in the car park – action packed
> day planned.
>   Rory x

Action packed? She instantly became curious and pondered on what to wear. Where was Rory taking her? Eventually she plumped for skinny jeans, a cream cashmere jumper and brown suede knee high boots. Her brown quilted jacket finished the outfit off nicely. With a spring in her step, she went to the kitchens and made herself tea and toast. Glancing at the kitchen clock told her she didn't have long before meeting Rory. Thankfully she'd managed to get cover after sending an urgent email first thing to her team. It wasn't like her to ask at such short notice, which was why the manager was willing to step in, assuming it was an emergency. Cassie refused to feel any guilt. To her it *was* of paramount importance – it was Rory's last day.

She made her way to the car park as instructed and immediately saw Rory sat in his sporty little car. The roof was down and he waved up at her. She smiled, noticing how devilishly handsome he looked sat behind the wheel in his fitted leather jacket.

'Ready to go?' he grinned, as she got in beside him.

'Where are we going?' Was he going to set off like this, with the roof down? she thought, wishing she was wearing a floaty scarf and dark shades, like they did in the films.

'My hometown, well city actually, Lancaster.'

'Ah, will I see your childhood home?'

'The full guided tour,' he answered, starting up the engine. Within minutes they were breezing along the country roads, blasting out Stereophonics.

'Maybe tomorrow, I'll find my way home...'

Cassie looked sideways at him. How apt were those lyrics?

It didn't take them too long to arrive over the bridge entering the city. She marvelled at the skyline, seeing the castle, the priory next door, the Ashton memorial and the church spires. It was a splendid, historic place, oozing with character. Lancaster had everything, links to the past, but also a lively student vibe. There was a canal and a quay built in the eighteenth century during its Golden Age as a port, and beautiful acres of parkland with enchanting woodland walks. Rory parked outside the castle.

'Come on, we'll go on a guided tour.'

Cassie enjoyed listening to the guide as they walked through the dark stone passageways, hearing about the trial of the Pendle witches, who had been imprisoned there centuries ago, in the cells at the bottom of the castle. The magnificent halls were still used as court rooms, which she found extraordinary.

'The castle and courts coexist,' the guide had told them. It was a touch eerie seeing where the criminals were hanged, but darkly interesting.

After the tour, Rory put an arm round her shoulders. 'Let's go for a drink.' He ushered her down the steps to an aged pub. They were actually underground. 'There's a secret tunnel from here to the castle,' he told her. 'It was used to store gunpowder at one time.'

'Really?' Cassie's eyes widened.

'Yes, then it became a cellar.'

Cassie could see three tunnels running from the bar area. It was easy to imagine all the wine bottles lining the curved walls. She found the whole experience amazing.

'Let's have lunch here,' she said, taken by her surroundings.

'OK,' he smiled.

'Let's sit...' she eyed each tunnel area; one was upmarket with raspberry-striped seating and tall tables, another more basic with wooden pews and stools; the middle tunnel was a comfortable dining area with spotlights and pale grey panelling. 'In here.' She made her way into the dining area.

Cassie sat back and enjoyed watching Rory order their food at the bar. He stood tall and confident, but in an unaffected way. He was friendly to the guy serving, asking for his recommendation of wine. She liked his easy manner, suspecting that not many of the finest barristers would have the same grounded way about them. She couldn't imagine the pompous, middle-class set asking what wine to buy.

'Here we are.' He passed her a glass of white while he'd ordered a cappuccino for himself. 'So, what do you think of Lancaster so far?'

'I've always liked it, but I've never been round the castle, and this is a fascinating old pub, isn't it?' Her eyes scanned the curved stone walls again.

'It is,' he nodded. 'Takes me back to my student days.' Then he blew on his coffee and took a gulp. Cassie laughed.

'What?' he asked, somewhat bemused at her response.

'You. You make me laugh.'

'*Why?*'

'I don't know.' She shrugged. 'Just your down-to-earth way, that's all.'

He frowned. 'Why shouldn't I be down to earth?'

'Because a lot of people in your position, wouldn't be. They'd be... superior, toffy—'

'Like your ex?' he cut in with a smirk.

'Yes,' she laughed again, 'like Justin.'

'Well,' he reached out for her hand and kissed it, 'I am most definitely not like that banker.' His blue eyes twinkled. Cassie let out another yelp of laughter.

The day continued with the same banter flowing as Rory pointed out different points of interest. They walked to Dalton Square, a lovely restful place with benches and trees scattered with tea lights; one would never guess it was where the infamous Dr Buck Ruxton had lived, making national news in the 1930s after murdering his wife and house maid. Rory then drove them past his old grammar school and on to his parents' house.

'I would call in, but they're staying at my brother's in Kent at the moment,' Rory explained. Cassie took in the modest semi-detached house off the main road and tried to picture a young Rory being brought up there. On the way back, he detoured past Lancaster University.

'It looks fairly modern, doesn't it?' she remarked at its flat angular roofs, with turquoise and orange walls.

'It is, I suppose, as universities go.'

Cassie didn't want the day to end, but dusk was setting in as they approached the Inn at Lilacwell. It had been magical spending time with Rory, but now a sad, empty sensation overcame her. He was going back to London in the morning. Then what? Tears stung her eyes and she bit her bottom lip in an attempt to stay composed. Rory sensed the shift in mood. He too was feeling low. He didn't want to leave her, especially given the experience she'd had with that dickhead Justin. After several minutes silence, he spoke.

'Listen, Cassie, I'll be back. I just need to concentrate on work at the moment.' He winced, regretting his choice of words, however true.

'I know,' she replied quietly.

'Once this business with the protesters is over, I'll have more time—' he stopped, cursing himself. He swallowed, then tried again, 'What I mean is, I don't want to distance myself.'

Cassie smiled weakly; well, he wasn't telling her anything she didn't already know, was he?

'I don't want you at a distance, Rory.' She saw him grip the steering wheel.

'Cassie, I'm going to make us work,' he stated with force, 'whatever it takes.' His jaw was set in determination.

And there it was; the promise she so wanted to believe. But could she?

Rory and Cassie entered the Inn hand in hand, causing a few raised eyebrows from a number of staff who'd seen them. Cassie was beyond caring. She went directly to the bar and ordered drinks, then they both sat at the table which Rory had reserved. Although they wanted to be together, there was a slight tension which was only natural given the circumstances. Both felt the same, they simply didn't want to part. Waves of misery kept surfacing, threatening to break the time they had left.

'Feels like the last supper,' Cassie attempted to lighten the atmosphere. It didn't.

'Don't say that, Cass.' Rory rubbed his eyes, emotionally drained.

'Are you hungry?' she asked.

'Not really.'

'Come on then, let's go up to my room. I can order sandwiches later.'

Once sat down on the settee, they automatically cuddled up together. 'I'll miss this,' she whispered.

'It's only for a short while.' His voice was thick. He kissed the top of her head.

'Promise?' her voice cracked.

'Oh, Cassie.' He nudged her to face him. 'I meant what I said. I'm going to make this work.'

'But how?' she croaked, tears on the verge of spilling. He inhaled a shaky sigh.

'Just trust me, Cass.' Her eyes searched his face, questioning him, but he gave nothing away. He reached under her chin and gently brought her face closer to his, then kissed her tenderly. She wrapped her arms round him tighter, wanting the warmth of his body against hers. They knew where this was inevitably leading, moving to her bed as one, both frantically undressing, each hungry for the other. Cassie stared at his broad chest, flat stomach and muscular thighs. His eyes blazed with passion, desperate to touch her smooth skin, dusted with freckles. He yearned to kiss every single one and taste her. Their mouths met in a frenzy, urgently kissing, as they explored one another's bodies. Cassie became aware of a faint buzzing sound in the background.

'W… what's that?' she gasped.

'Ignore it,' he grunted, as his tongue flicked her earlobe, sending her body into a jolt. The noise wouldn't stop. Rory lifted his head and looked to the floor, where his phone had fallen out of his jeans pocket. It lay there lit up, buzzing furiously. He saw the caller. Shit. He stopped still. Cassie opened her eyes to see him reach out to pick it up. 'Sorry, Cassie.' He looked at her, full of regret, then answered. 'Yes?' His face dropped. 'When?' He closed his eyes. 'I'm on my way. Say nothing to the press. Absolutely nothing. Bye.'

Cassie stared. 'What's happened?'

'The tunnel's collapsed. One of the activists has been taken to hospital.'

'Oh no!' she cried. 'What about the others?'

'They escaped in time. Heavy rainfall caused it.' He ran his hands through his hair. 'I… I've got to go, Cass.' He started to get dressed.

'Of course,' she quickly got up and reached for her clothes. She saw how pale his face was and started to panic. 'Rory, please drive safely, won't you?'

'Yeah, I'll pack, then set off.' He made for his room and Cassie soon followed. He quickly shoved all his clothes and toiletries into his suitcase, all the time his mind was whirling. He knew what lay ahead of him in London and was trying to keep calm. Now more than ever he needed a clear head. He zipped up the case and picked it up off the bed. 'Right, I'm going, Cassie.'

She quickly ran to him and threw her arms round his body. 'Please, please be careful,' she pleaded, not wanting to let go.

'Hey, hey.' He calmly unwrapped her to face him. 'Don't worry.' Then he kissed her. 'Remember what I said, yeah?' He spoke softly, hating to see her so upset. A tear fell down her cheek. He wiped it away with this thumb. 'I'll ring as soon as I get back.'

'Yes, you must,' she choked.

'Please, Cass, don't cry.'

'S... sorry,' she gulped, trying to regain control.

'OK, I'm off.' With one more kiss he went. She didn't want to say goodbye in the car park, where everyone would see them, so she stayed in her room and waited and waited for him to contact her.

Chapter 12

Fletcher put another log on the fire. He had a feeling this evening was about to be a long one. Lilly and Ruby were coming to discuss the holiday. It had been all Lilly had talked about since his suggestion of her twin sister joining them. Quite how it was all going to pan out, Fletcher wasn't sure. Already he was having reservations, but it was too late now, both sisters were clearly revved up for it. To back out would be cruel. So, here he was, preparing to meet them. Together, they could be a formidable force, firmly lead by Ruby, who was the eldest twin by thirty-four minutes; a fact she regularly reminded Lilly of. Ruby didn't mince her words and that was putting it mildly. Fletcher nicknamed her Boudicca, but never quite had the guts to call her that face to face.

He poured himself a large whisky. He was going to need it. Next door in the library, he could hear Adira and Jasper, busy making wedding plans no doubt. At that, he smiled contently. He, more than most, was delighted with Jasper's choice of bride. From the moment he had met Adira, parked with her campervan on his land, he knew she was special. He laughed to himself at the stir that lass had created in Lilacwell when first arriving. The herbal medicine she'd administered had caused much speculation within the village. Very soon she'd become the 'go-to girl' with her healing potions. The one thing she hadn't needed any medicine for was capturing Jasper's heart. That had been done without any assistance at all. Quite naturally they had been drawn together, which had pleased him immensely.

Feeling sentimental, Fletcher considered his relationship with Lilly. Up until now, he'd always looked upon her as his old friend, someone to share his memories with, as he had grown up with Lilly and Ruby. With Lilly, though, there had been a close bond. When she'd offered to assist at The Laurels, he'd been pleased of not only the help, but having the time to chat and reminisce about the old days. Together they would while away the time, chuckling over the past. Occasionally it would be interrupted by subdued reflection, as though privately, in their quieter moments, a feeling of what might have been had caused them to stop and think. This was certainly true of Fletcher, but then, wasn't it his fault that he and Lilly had never taken the plunge? He, to his detriment, had been obsessed with his brother's wife, Alice. Of course, it hadn't helped knowing it had been reciprocated.

She had been his, but only for one night. Precisely one month later, Alice declared she was pregnant. Fletcher had been elated, convinced the baby was his. But his elation soon turned to dismay when learning that Alice was not going to leave Rufus, and that she couldn't be sure who the father actually was; only that it was a Hendricks. That had been the party line, but they both knew, deep down, that Fletcher most probably was Jasper's father.

Fletcher had only recently revealed this to Jasper and, after the revelation, they had decided to leave things as the status quo. What was the point in dragging up old history that would only cause hurt and pain to all involved? So, officially Jasper remained Fletcher's nephew, but as the sole inheritor to The Laurels, it really didn't make much difference. Most important was that Jasper knew how very much loved he was by Fletcher.

He took another mouthful of whisky. A wedding would give them all a boost; a good old family knees up. His thoughts were interrupted by Ruby.

'Where is he?' she demanded, her loud voice reverberating round the hallway.

'Fletcher's in the drawing room, lighting a fire,' Adira replied.

'Good. It's enough to catch your death of cold in this place. Always was an ice box,' Ruby threw back.

'This way dear, don't make a fuss,' intervened Lilly, ushering her into the room.

'Ladies!' Fletcher knocked back the rest of his whisky. 'Come and take a seat.'

'I'll have one of those,' Ruby nodded towards his glass.

'Oh, yes, certainly.' He made his way to the drinks cabinet.

'It'll help take the chill off my bones,' she further complained with a sniff.

Fletcher rolled his eyes and poured them all a whisky, giving himself a double. With a deep breath he braced himself and turned to face them.

'Well, are we ready to make plans for our exciting river cruise?' he asked with forced enthusiasm and a false smile.

'River cruise?' said Ruby with a raised eyebrow. 'I don't think so, Fletcher. We were thinking more of the Highlands—'

'Oh, well…' Lilly tried to interrupt.

'Shush, Lilly,' barked Ruby, then continued, arms folded, shoulders back, 'Fletcher, we're far too old to be frolicking on the Danube. No, we think something closer to home would be more suitable, Scotland.'

'Scotland?' replied Fletcher, gobsmacked.

'Yes, a castle in Scotland,' Ruby told him resolutely.

'A castle?' Fletcher blinked.

'Oh, a castle, how romantic!' Lilly clapped her hands in glee.

Clearly this was news to her, too. So much for the 'we think', thought Fletcher sourly. What on God's earth had he let himself in for?

—

Jasper and Adira looked at each other and burst into giggles.

'A castle in Scotland!' hissed Adira.

'I know,' Jasper shook his head. 'The old boy didn't see that coming.'

The pair of them couldn't help but overhear the conversation in the drawing room, especially given Ruby's piercing, authoritarian tone.

'He's met his match with Ruby,' laughed Adira.

'Hasn't he just, poor bloke.' Then he turned to look at the wedding magazines on the desk in front of him. Adira had shown him the winter season issues, to give him an idea of what she had in mind. Pictures of cosy lit rooms, bathed in candlelight, decked with ivy, blooming with roses, holly and berries; silver trays holding crystal glasses of mulled wine; white muslin-covered tables set with porcelain, cut-glass and a twinkling candelabra. It was all so magical and Adira had completely fallen for it. She envisaged the orangery at The Laurels as the perfect venue to host such an occasion.

'What do you think?' she waited with bated breath for Jasper's answer.

'I think…'

'Yes?'

'It's perfect,' he said sitting back, enjoying the beaming smile light up her face. Was this beautiful, clever creature really going to be his wife?

'It will be perfect,' she agreed. 'I've applied for the licence. We need to set a date and get the registrar booked.'

'Right.' Jasper reached for his diary in the desk drawer. Adira moved to look over his shoulder. Various meetings and business appointments filled December, but the weekends were free.

'Let's go for the twenty-first, winter solstice,' said Adira.

'The shortest day?'

'Yes, I want it dark early for the fireworks.'

Jasper smiled wryly to himself. Of course she'd want fireworks.

'That's settled then, the twenty-first of December. What time?'

'Ideally late afternoon, followed by an early evening dinner, but I suppose I'd better check with the registrar first.'

'OK, I'll leave it in your capable hands.'

Adira was happy to oversee the wedding plans, knowing how occupied Jasper was with the business. The sale of The Cobbled Courtyard was almost due for completion and he also had estate matters to see to.

'I've got a few thoughts for the wedding package we can offer at The Laurels.' Adira's head had been brimming with ideas whilst researching for her own.

'Great. Hopefully in the summer we can advertise it on the website.'

It was all coming together, they made such a good team. Jasper was impressed with the way Adira had calmly and efficiently pitched in with running The Laurels estate. They worked side by side seamlessly, each valuing the other's opinion. Not many brides would have been so accommodating in cancelling a summer wedding, to hastily reschedule with only a few months' notice. They were open and honest with each other; however, there was one secret that Jasper was keeping to himself. Adira deserved a decent honeymoon and she was going to get one. He was at pains to keep it under wraps and surprise her on their big day.

Chapter 13

Goldgate Gardens were barricaded off. Outside in the square a hive of reporters circulated. Camera crews had set up and tension hung in the air like a thundercloud. Eviction proceedings had begun. An activist above ground, who had built a makeshift shelter in one of the trees, shouted to the press.

'Living in a tunnel is dangerous. But when people are really, really desperate, this is what they are forced to resort to. We are all going to die if action isn't taken to address the climate emergency!'

The tunnellers had worked in shifts round the clock using pickaxes, shovels and buckets. The tunnel had been shored up with wooden joists and thick boards. However, heavy rainpours had weakened the support and the tunnel had given way. Three of the four activists had managed to escape in time, but tragically the last one had been crushed by the earth as it tumbled onto him halfway out of the entrance. Firefighters had managed to dig the protester out, who thankfully was still breathing and was immediately rushed to hospital. There he lay in intensive care, but was reported to be in a stable condition. The remaining protesters had then pitched tents or erected tree shelters near the tunnel opening. The construction company, in the interim, had taken legal temporary possession of

Goldgate Gardens in order to progress with works necessary for the building of the new carriageway.

'These protests are a danger to the safety of the protesters, our staff and the general public, and put unnecessary strain on the emergency services,' a spokesperson for the company stated to the reporters. They added that their security team was trained in use of force.

Meanwhile, in court, two charges of aggravated trespass and one of criminal damage were being heard. Counsel for the prosecution spoke of 'The actions of these illegal trespassers putting their own lives at risk, as well as the lives of the construction staff, agents and service personnel who worked around the clock to ensure the wellbeing of people who placed themselves in such a dangerous situation underground.'

To which Rory, as defending counsel retorted, 'These defendants never committed the offence of aggravated trespass. There was no evidence of any constructor or construction taking place on the land at the time the tunnel was being dug.'

The opposing side then threw comments of how 'This case was an enormous waste of public money from individuals who acted dangerously and irresponsibly.'

Rory shot back, 'These individuals care deeply for the planet and are of strong, moral fibre.'

To the jubilation of the crowds now congregating on Goldgate Gardens, the District Judge had dismissed the charges in relation to the high-profile protest, on the basis that, as the construction company's aim was to first clear the area, it hadn't actually been carrying out any construction work on the site at the time the charges were levelled against the activists. Therefore, the court did not find fit to convict.

The crowds went wild on hearing the good news. Rory was met with a thunderous applause outside the court buildings. Cameras flashing shone in his eyes as he tried to make an exit.

'Rory, what are your feelings on the verdict?' hounded a reporter, shoving a microphone to his mouth.

'As I have always maintained, my clients are defenders of the earth. They ought to be commended for their valiant efforts.'

'Are you going to celebrate in style?' asked another.

'No,' he replied calmly, looking straight into their camera, 'I am going to the hospital, to see the injured activist.'

A short silence followed, then as he stormed past them all down the steps, they quickly pursued him until he made it into his car and drove off.

In the quiet peacefulness whilst driving, Rory reflected on the day's events. It had all gone to plan, well almost. Timing, that had been key. He had advised the activists on when to start digging the tunnel, *before* the construction work had started. He had orchestrated the whole thing, but what he hadn't foreseen was the extreme weather. He couldn't have controlled that. And now an innocent man lay in hospital. Rory Molloy, the maverick barrister might have won in court today, but it was with a heavy heart.

He arrived back in his flat after a brief visit to the hospital, and as he put his key in the front door, a neighbour shouted across the street.

'Good work, Rory!'

He turned and smiled bleakly. All he wanted to do was sink into a hot bath – with Cassie. Just the thought of her gave him some comfort. That, and being told by the hospital staff that the poor man caught in the tunnel was now making good progress. Thank God. Rory wearily climbed the stairs to his apartment. He was dog tired. The past two weeks had been the most stressful of his career. Not just poring over law books well into the night, but having to handle the press and all the attention such a high-profile case brought. Articles of him kept appearing on social media, covering his background. Some had published photos of him in his student days on various demos. He was branded the 'Climate Warrior' and had even been approached to give an interview on a popular TV talk show. Rory hated the attention. Loathed it, in fact, knowing full well how it could have played out, had he lost his court battle. The world seemed so fickle, as well as brittle. His main objective had been accomplished, to publicise the climate crisis; it appeared the whole nation had watched with interest the commotion at Goldgate Gardens. Everyone had an opinion, whether they supported the activists or not, and the issue had been brought to the forefront of conversations, debating for or against. Rory hadn't quite counted on the amount of coverage *he* was receiving though, which was beginning to trouble him.

He reached into the fridge for a beer, in dire need of relaxing. After knocking back half a bottle of Stella his phone rang. It was Cassie on FaceTime.

'Hi, you OK?' she frowned, looking concerned.

'Not bad. Just exhausted.'

'You look it,' she replied, then added, 'but still handsome.' Cassie had seen him on the news, her chest pounding with pride.

'Good to know,' he smiled, rubbing his eyes. He wanted her here, now, next to him, so much it hurt.

'Rory?'

'Hmm.' He threw the rest of his beer back.

'I want to see you,' she spoke in a small voice.

'I know, Cass, and I want to see you but—'

'You're too busy,' she finished.

It killed him to hear her sound so despondent, but there was no way he could leave London at the moment.

'It won't always be like this, Cassie. I promise.'

'Sorry, you don't need this right now, do you?'

No, he really didn't. He was stuck in an impossible situation over which he had no control and the resentment was starting to build. And at that precise moment he made a decision. The realisation of knowing it was the right one instantly made the tension inside him evaporate. All the pent-up anxiety slowly started to ebb away.

'Rory? Are you still here?' he looked miles away.

'Yes,' he smiled, 'I'll always be here for you.'

She gave a tiny squeak of emotion. 'Oh, Rory...' she said in a strangled voice.

'Listen, I'll be with you very soon, OK?'

'Yes, OK,' she gulped.

'I'll ring you tomorrow.'

'Yes, now you get some rest, you Climate Warrior, you,' she teased.

'Give me a break,' he laughed. He was about to say something else, but stopped himself. Cassie sensed it.

'What?' she asked.

'Nothing. Speak tomorrow.'

She blew him a kiss and he winked back before ending the call.

He'd shocked himself at what he wanted to say. Was it because he feared she doubted him? Did Cassie think he was another Justin figure? His reasons for not seeing her were genuine, as were his feelings. It startled him at how much he did care, given the length of time he'd known her. Cassie, he believed, thought the same way. He pictured her clinging onto him, begging him to drive safely the night he had to leave Lilacwell. A strong bond had been formed, one which he intended to protect, at all costs. Typical Rory, he'd fallen too deeply too fast, but wasn't that what he was renowned for? He was impulsive, passionate, focused and fiercely loyal. Adira had been right; when Rory wanted something, he'd fight tooth and nail to get it – and he wanted Cassie.

–

Cassie replayed the news on her streaming app, wanting to see Rory. She paused it on the close up of his face. He really did look knackered, with dark rings circling his eyes. She felt guilty for putting pressure on him. Should she really be expecting him to travel up north when he was so busy? Under the circumstances she thought it best to go the distance, providing she'd be allowed the annual leave.

She made her way to reception, seeing Lisa on the way down.

'Hi Lisa, you all right?' She seemed to be getting bigger by the day.

'Well… could I have a word please?'

'Of course, come into the office.' Cassie led the way to the small room opposite the reception area. She closed the door behind them. 'Take a seat, Lisa.'

'Thanks.' She hesitated then continued, 'The thing is, I was wondering if you'd consider me for the clerical post advertised.'

Cassie looked surprised. 'But won't you be on maternity leave?'

'Well, yes, but long term I expect to come back to work, albeit reduced hours. I'd like to be more involved with the admin side of things.'

'I see,' Cassie nodded her head. 'Don't you like your current job?'

'I want to progress. I would also like to earn more.'

Cassie liked her spirit. Being pregnant wasn't going to hinder her, and why should it? Plus the increase in salary would be welcome with a new baby.

'In that case, Lisa, yes. I think we could work something out. Can I ask what childcare you have planned once the baby's arrived?'

'My husband is reducing his hours, so between us we should manage. He's keen to spend as much time as possible with the baby.' She looked down at her growing bump. 'We've waited a long time for it.'

A wave of compassion hit Cassie. She admired the young couple who clearly were going to make doting parents.

'Right, well, seeing as no one so far has applied for the job, I'll take it off the website. We could start to train you now, if you like. It would make sense.'

'Yes!' Lisa agreed in delight.

'To be honest I was worried about you housekeeping now.' She nodded towards Lisa's swollen abdomen with a smile. 'How long to go?'

'Three months,' beamed Lisa. 'And… thanks Cassie, this means a lot to me.' She patted her bump. 'To my family.'

Cassie swallowed the lump in her throat before replying. 'My pleasure. Let's start with the purchase orders, shall we?'

After a busy morning showing Lisa various admin duties, Cassie was pleased with the progress she'd made. Lisa proved to be a very fast learner, eager to take on the new responsibilities. She reminded Cassie of her early days in the hotel. She needed to update the manager of the new arrangement, which would mean advertising for a new housekeeping post, plus ask for annual leave. The Inn wasn't full, so she didn't think it would cause any problems. Cassie planned to surprise Rory with an impromptu visit. She only hoped he wouldn't be too tired to accommodate her. A warmth rushed through her body remembering the last time they'd been together. The image of his naked body was enough to hotfoot it to London.

Chapter 14

Fletcher stared at the itinerary in front of him. It was a done deal. Ruby had arranged everything; the all-inclusive five-day break in Ayrshire; the hotel, an impressive castle set in two thousand acres of Scottish highland; and the transport, a coach. They were going the first week in December, when apparently, 'the castle will be adorned with glitz and glamour for the Christmas festivities.'

He'd been bulldozed into it, without any say. The only input he had was handing over the credit card Ruby had requested. The cheek of the woman! Still, it had bucked Lilly up no end, listening to her excited chatter of the fun they were going to have. Fletcher had to bite his tongue. He'd go with the flow and try his best to enjoy it for her sake if nothing else. At least it would be a change of scenery, even if it meant having to tolerate Boudicca.

He must admit, though, browsing the hotel brochure, Ruby had made an exceedingly good choice. It did look the ultimate tranquil escape.

> Crowned with battlements and turrets, Glen-rick Castle is the epitome of baronial grandeur. Nestled between lofty mountains, it stands in direct contrast to its sumptuous interior. Spacious individually

designed rooms, a Michelin star restaurant, luxurious spa and whisky bar…

Whisky bar! Now you're talking, thought Fletcher with cheer. He read on,

> …over eighty varieties of the quintessential Scottish drop. Take a taste tour of artisan techniques and regional distinction.

Too bloody right, he rubbed his hands in glee.

'Tea break, Fletcher!' Lilly called, entering the room carrying a tray. On noticing the brochure she broke into a wide smile. 'Ah, looking at our castle?' She put the tray down and stood behind him to get a proper look. There it was, looking majestic, standing proudly on the Scottish glens amongst the pink and lavender heather. 'I've never been anywhere so… magical,' she gasped, making Fletcher's heart melt. It was worth it, every single penny to see Lilly this happy.

–

Adira was making good progress with the wedding. She had booked the registrar for the date of her choice and the venue licence to hold civil marriages and partnership ceremonies at The Laurels had been granted. Having the licence was going to open up a whole new dimension to the business. Obviously, they would have to specialise in small, intimate weddings as the orangery could only hold approximately thirty people, but with the glamping site next door, many guests would be able to join the celebrations after the ceremony. The shepherds huts and tents could accommodate a large number of people. Catering-wise, Adira thought hog roasts in summer on the field, and maybe wedding breakfasts in the dining room, hopefully with a local catering company to oversee the food.

The next job was to organise a photographer for her own big day. This would need particular care; their photos would appear on the website to advertise the wedding package. Everything had to look its absolute best – The Laurels, the orangery, plus the gardens and grounds. Adira had decided she wanted a minimal, tasteful wedding dress, nothing too elaborate with frills and layers, just elegant and chic. However, finding what she had in mind was proving difficult. Nothing seemed to grab her. They were either too fussy with mountains of lace and sequins, too revealing with plunging necklines and transparent voile, or too dramatic being backless with fishtails. She hadn't seen anything so far which fit the bill. Jasper, meanwhile, was easy to sort. Both he and Fletcher were going to wear grey morning suits. Fletcher was to be best man, much to his delight. Adira wasn't having a bridesmaid and the guests would be immediate family only. She fully intended to keep the day as low key as possible. As long as they were married, that was all that mattered, not the pomp and ceremony that often got caught up in wedding plans.

Jasper had a little more vigour. The sale of The Cobbled Courtyard had completed and the last of the campers had now vacated The Laurels Hideaway glamping site. It amazed them just how many hearty backpackers and travellers there were that loved the great outdoors, despite the winter nights creeping in.

Adira was looking forward to putting the wedding package together. In her mind's eye she imagined the web page with the orangery blooming with colourful flora in summer, fresh cut lawns, bunting swooping through the trees, bistro sets covered with gingham tablecloths and in winter it being lit with candles and lanterns, a full moon shining down from an inky, star-scattered sky... She was going to market The Laurels to its full potential. The interior of the dining room would lend itself perfectly for a more formal venue, with its oak panelling, high ceiling with ornamental coving and chandelier. The polished mahogany table running the full length of the room, surrounded by matching chairs was ideal for a sit-down wedding meal. Her thoughts were interrupted by the ringing of her phone.

'Hello darling, how are you?' It was Edie, her grand-mother.

'Hi Gran, lovely to hear from you. I'm fine thanks, and you?'

Her gran caught up on the various goings-on in her life before getting to the real reason of her call. 'I was wondering how the wedding plans are going.'

'I'm getting there, apart from the dress.'

'Why's that?'

'There's nothing I like the look of. What happened to the good old-fashioned, simple and stylish look?'

'Like mine, you mean?' joked Edie.

'Exactly, your wedding dress was beautiful.' Adira recalled the photos of her grandmother's wedding day. Edie looked a stunning bride in her vintage, ivory lace tea dress.

'I've still got it,' she laughed.

'Really?'

'Yes, it's packed up somewhere. I couldn't part with it, too many happy memories.'

An idea suddenly sprang to Adira's mind.

'Gran, can I have it?' she asked excitedly.

'What? My wedding dress?'

'Yes. Do you think it will fit me?'

'Err… I think so. We could have it altered though, if need be. I'll get it cleaned first.'

'Oh, would you?'

'Of course, then you'll have to come and try it for size.'

'Great! Thanks, Gran.'

'My pleasure.' Edie smiled, pleased her beloved dress was getting another outing after all these years, and who better to wear it than her granddaughter?

—

At The Cobbled Courtyard, Jasper was finding it fascinating to see each tenant tailor their craft, from the robust carvings of Crafty Carpentry to the delicate ceramics of The Bolthole. Jessie, the potter, chatted to Jasper, explaining how it was time for her to retire.

'I've loved living and working here, but the arthritis plays up now. I can't use the potter's wheel like I used to. It's time to go.' She gave a sad smile to Jasper, creasing the wrinkles in her face and looked wistfully round the room. Jessie had lived in the flat above the studio, as did Max above the forge.

'Well, you've certainly earned your retirement, Jessie,' replied Jasper. The old folk of Lilacwell undoubtedly had some staying power, he thought, considering how Fletcher had plodded on to the bitter end, before finally handing the baton over to him. They were made of strong stuff, that's for sure. He only hoped he'd be the same.

Max was in the forge, bashing away at a piece of iron when Jasper walked in. The temperature of the furnace hit him instantly. A great hissing sound came from the tank of water as Max dipped in the hot metal causing a cloud of steam around them.

'Jasper,' he nodded, wiping his wet face, smeared with black soot.

'Hi, Max.' Jasper looked at what he was holding. 'What are you making?'

'Cast-iron curtain poles.'

'Ah, right.' Jasper admired the ornate twirls on the end of the pole that only a master craftsman could produce. He understood why Max didn't want to have any hassle running the Courtyard, being happy to spend all his time in the forge where his talent lay. He took a look around, taking in all the sturdy equipment that had years of use in them: anvils, chisels, tongs, hammers, plus lots of other tools. 'What does that do?' he asked, pointing to what looked like a steel pyramid on a rail.

'It's a flatter,' explained Max. 'Flattens the surface of metal.' He smiled to himself. He'd clocked Jasper's appraisal and couldn't imagine him getting his hands quite as dirty as himself.

'Fancy a coffee? I'm popping into the cafe next,' asked Jasper.

'Better finish these, thanks,' replied Max, picking up his hammer to start bashing again.

Leaving Max to his work, Jasper headed to the cafe and ordered a coffee. Tom served him and brought it over to the table by the window where Jasper sat looking out. He was observing the wooden statue of the Green Man standing outside the carpentry workshop. It was intricately carved with his long, wild hair and beard, face covered with foliage. What was the Green Man supposed to symbolise? pondered Jasper. Ah yes, it was the circle of life, death and rebirth. He narrowed his eyes in contemplation, wondering if this had any significance to Fitz, the owner of the workshop. He was reminded of how he had to get to know all the occupants of The Cobbled Courtyard as their landlord.

Jasper's gaze then followed the customers milling through the studios. It was quite an eclectic crowd, from young to old, couples, families to single people taking in the wares of the craft shops. It was good to see such custom, proving The Cobbled Courtyard was a thriving business.

Before leaving, Jasper called at The Fresh Bouquet to buy Adira a bunch of flowers. James, the florist, was a very well-spoken, pleasant chap, who insisted on calling him Mr Hendricks.

'What do you recommend?' he asked James.

'Might I ask if the flowers are for a special occasion, Mr Hendricks?' replied James.

'Not particularly, just want to surprise her,' smiled Jasper.

'Then I suggest a pale cabbage rose bouquet, with deep green euphorbia foliage?' said James with gusto, pointing to the said flowers in the shop.

'Sounds good,' replied Jasper, trying to keep a straight face.

All in all, Jasper had enjoyed his visit getting to know the merry band at the Courtyard. They seemed a decent, genuine bunch of people he could do business with. Everyone seemed to gel together well and he was looking forward to being part of the team. Jasper was keen to fit in and wanted to be thought of as a good landlord, not someone to be wary of or avoided. He knew the family name was important to uphold here in Lilacwell. The Hendricks had always employed local people.

Chapter 15

Rory was greeted by the Head of Chambers, Nigel Kerfoot, as he entered the general office.

'Ah Rory, might I have a word?'

Just looking at the man set Rory's teeth on edge. 'Of course.' He followed him to his office. Nigel discreetly shut the door and sat behind his enormous desk.

'Well, Rory, you've made quite an impression,' he said, giving one of his sickly smiles.

'Have I?' Rory flatly replied.

'Oh come, come. Don't be coy.' Nigel forced a brittle laugh. 'You're the talk of the Law Society, which,' he nodded his head in approval, 'isn't doing us any harm. In fact, you've put the chambers in a very good light. Excelled its already fine reputation, one might say.' He smiled again. Rory noticed it never quite reached his eyes, though. Was this praise given resentfully? Did he even care? He stared, saying nothing. Nigel coughed, as if waiting for some response. 'So... I've decided, that is, we, the chambers have decided that in future all high-profile cases are given to you.'

There was a slight pause. Rory stared at him and said nothing. Nigel smirked to himself, misunderstanding Rory's silence for him being overwhelmed.

'Of course, this will mean more spotlight, but as we've already seen,' he gave a shallow chuckle making Rory wince, 'you're no stranger to that. You manage the press extremely well, don't you?'

'I'd manage a pay rise better,' replied Rory acidly, then added, 'Any assistance with all these *high-profile* cases?'

'Of course not,' cut in Nigel swiftly, making Rory snort at the injustice.

Nigel blinked. This was hardly the reaction he'd been expecting. A slow anger started to rise up inside him.

'Do you understand exactly what I am offering you, Molloy?' he said in a low, menacing voice.

'Yeah, I do. More work for less money,' replied Rory staring him in the face, refusing to be intimidated. 'I don't want them.' He folded his arms defiantly.

'Sorry?' Nigel looked perplexed. 'What do you mean you don't want them?'

'Just that. I. Don't. Want. Them. Which word are you struggling with, Nigel?'

'I... how dare you?' he spluttered, eyes bulging in outrage.

'Oh, I dare all right,' retorted, Rory standing. 'Had I lost in court, you wouldn't have thought twice in hurling me out of this chamber on me arse.' Nigel recoiled at the vulgar expression. 'I'm quitting, Nigel. You can shove this chamber where the sun don't shine.' And with that, Rory strode out of the office, slamming the door behind him.

Nigel's eyes narrowed. Who did the jumped-up nobody think he was? He coolly picked up his phone.

'Clear Rory Molloy's desk and have security escort him from the building.' Strictly speaking the little shit should give a month's notice, but there was no way he'd ever step foot in his chambers again.

Rory was handed the cardboard box containing his possessions. He accepted them with open arms.

'Thank you so much,' he beamed and walked head held high out of Goldgate Chambers for the last time, with all his colleagues looking on, jaws dropped.

As the cool air met him on the steps outside, Rory inhaled a deep breath and took a good look round at Goldgate Square for the last time. Everything was ticking along normally, oblivious to the life-changing decision he'd just made. People were wandering in and out of the artisan shops, the little deli was bustling with early lunch time diners and Mario's wine bar, which he'd often frequented, was starting to fill. All nice enough, but it wasn't the north. It wasn't home. He turned for a final look at the chambers, the huge red bricked building standing proudly with its mirrored glass lettering, announcing smugly the fine establishment it was. Well good luck to it, thought Rory. It wasn't for him, and it had taken one trip to Lancashire and one good woman to make him realise. He'd never really been happy in London. Yes, it had provided an illustrious career which had earned him money, but Rory wasn't particularly materialistic. It hadn't been enough to tempt him to stay and grow roots. Already he was feeling much better in himself, lighter in mood and spirit. Of course, he knew that the initial sense of freedom was temporary and in the longer term he needed to take stock and make future plans, but for now, he intended to enjoy every minute of the euphoria.

On the drive back home, Rory's head was catching up with what his heart had done. He'd have to sell his flat. That wasn't going to be a problem; property in the area of north London where he lived sold like hot cakes. There'd be a tidy profit to be made, too. He also had a decent amount of savings accumulated over the years. The one advantage of not enjoying a London lifestyle despite living in the city had been the money stacking up whilst staying in. This was going to provide space and time for him to think about where and what he was going to do next. It didn't worry him. The visceral feeling in his gut told him he had absolutely made the right choice in leaving the chambers. He also knew beyond any doubt whatsoever that leaving London was the right move. Onwards and upwards!

Pulling up outside Hollins House he saw the back of someone standing in the entrance by the front door, ringing one of the flat buzzers. He blinked and looked again. Could it be? Surely not. But he, more than most, would know that sexy pixie cut anywhere.

'Cassie?' he called, slamming his car door shut. She turned suddenly and gave a wide smile.

'Rory!' She quickly ran down the steps and went to hug him.

'Cassie, what are you doing here?' he laughed, not quite believing his eyes as his arms wrapped round her.

'I couldn't keep away,' she muffled into his neck, then pulled back to kiss him. It was hot and urgent, both so needy of each other. Rory was caught up in the moment; just as he thought his day couldn't get any better, here she was. Finally he released her.

'Come inside, Pixie, and explain yourself.'

Together they walked up the stairs to his flat. As soon as they were inside, they kissed again — unable to resist — before Rory took her overnight bag from her.

'So, this is where you live, then?' said Cassie, her eyes scanned the room. It was nice enough, but lacked a woman's touch, she thought. There didn't seem to be any warmth or character to it, just clean and functional.

'Yeah, but it's not home,' he replied, guessing what she was thinking. 'The best thing's the communal garden.'

Cassie moved to the large bay window facing the back, overlooking the small green space.

'That is nice.' She took in the neatly cut lawn lit by ornate lampposts, surrounded by benches and flower beds. 'You wouldn't expect to see such a pretty garden judging from the front of the house.'

'No, it's what made me buy this place.' And now he was about to sell it. He had so much to tell her, but the twinkle in her eye told him they weren't going to have that conversation too soon. She moved closer to him with a surreptitious smile. He raised an eyebrow. She softly placed her lips on his. 'Are you leading me astray, Miss Wright?' he asked hoarsely.

'Hmm, yes I am,' she giggled, enjoying the power she had over him. Unable to endure any more, he groaned and lifted her up into his arms, then carried her to his bedroom. Booting the door shut behind him, he laid her on his bed. God, she was beautiful. Nothing and nobody was going to interrupt him this time. The place could burn down for all he cared, he wasn't moving from this room.

'That was incredible,' he whispered, kissing her gently on the forehead.

'I know,' she whispered back. A tear spilled from the corner of her eye.

'Hey, don't cry, Cass.' He kissed it away.

'I'm so happy,' she gulped.

'So am I,' he choked, then eased himself to lay next to her. He pulled her onto his chest and held her. Was now the time to tell her everything? But the slow, rhythmic breathing escaping from her told him she would soon be asleep. Tomorrow they would talk.

—

A bright sunshine shimmered through the curtains, waking Cassie. For a second she wondered where she was before feeling the heavy, warm body beside her. Rory's arm lay stretched across her chest, as if pinning her down as his possession. Cassie gently removed it, whilst managing not to stir him. She gazed at his contented face, slumbering peacefully. He was so handsome with his dark stubble and black locks falling over his forehead. As if sensing being watched, Rory slowly opened his eyes and smiled at her.

She leant over and kissed him. 'Good morning.'

'Hmm, it certainly is,' he mumbled, stretching and yawning.

'Shouldn't you be at work?' Cassie nodded towards the clock on the bedside cabinet telling them it was nine thirty.

'Nope.'

'Oh, why?'

'Coffee first, then I'll fill you in.' He pulled the covers back and got out of bed. Cassie admired his pert, bare bottom and broad shoulders before he pulled on a T-shirt and jeans.

Whilst Rory made them breakfast, Cassie dressed and went to join him. He looked very domesticated in the kitchenette, stood over the hob.

'I was going to bring you breakfast in bed,' he told her.

'No need. Let's have it here, overlooking the garden.'

Cassie sat at the two-seater table by the bay window and Rory placed two plates of scrambled eggs on toast down, then went back for coffees and sat down opposite her.

'This looks lovely, thanks.' Cassie was ravenous, she hadn't eaten since lunchtime yesterday. 'So,' she said between mouthfuls, 'tell me what's going on.' Rory wiped his mouth with the back of his hand.

'I've quit my job,' he explained without any fuss. Cassie dropped her folk.

'You… what?' she gaped at him in shock.

Rory shrugged. 'I've left the chambers, told them where to go.'

'But… but *why*?' She was reeling at the news but Rory simply looked at her calmly.

'Because I couldn't stand it a moment longer. I'm sick of the workload and the time given to it. But most of all I'm sick of the idiots I have to work with. Well, one idiot really, the Head of Chambers. Do you know, he actually offered me *more* cases, no mention of any pay rise or assistance though.'

'So… what are you going to do?' Cassie was still trying to comprehend his actions.

'Leave London.' This caused Cassie to splutter. Taking a drink of coffee, she cleared her throat before speaking again.

'But Rory, this is so sudden… I…'

'I thought you'd be pleased,' he replied, a touch surprised.

'I am!' she quickly replied. 'It's just so unexpected…'

'Didn't I tell you I was going to make us work?' He was looking directly at her again with a frown.

'Yes… yes you did…'

'Then why sound surprised?'

'I just never thought you'd do something so drastic, so *soon*.' Adira's words echoed in her mind, '*There's got to be a way round it*.' Had she predicted Rory acting this impetuously? She knew him pretty well after all. Then another thought occurred to her, making her shift uncomfortably. Rory frowned, sensing her unease.

'What's the matter?'

'Rory, you won't regret this will you? I'd never forgive myself if you did.'

'No.' he shook his head fervently, 'It just took you to make me see how unhappy I was. I don't belong here in London.'

'But your job – you're a brilliant barrister.'

'Yes, I am,' he grinned. 'But there are chambers in the north, Cass.'

Cassie stared at him. She opened her mouth to say something, then closed it. Oh my God. He'd done it. He'd really done it. Rory had quit his high-flying career at Goldgate Chambers to relocate near to her. She was speechless, yet so elated.

'I… I don't know what to say.' Tears stung her eyes. Rory, by contrast, was cool, calm and collected.

He gave her a lazy, sexy smile. 'I always think actions speak louder than words.'

Cassie chuckled, getting his drift. 'Then let me,' she said in her most seductive voice, taking his hand and leading him back to the bedroom.

After more blissful lovemaking, they lay cuddled up together.

'Rory?'

'Hmm?'

'Have you no doubts at all?'

'About my resignation, leaving London or us?' he asked.

'All three.'

'Hey.' He nudged her to look at him. 'None at all.'

'Some might say you've sacrificed too much for someone you've only known a short while.' She searched his face.

'It feels longer, though, doesn't it?'

'Yes. It does.' Then she gave a wry smile. 'Perhaps it's because I've been stalking you on your chambers' website for months.'

He laughed. 'And I you, on yours.'

'Really?' she asked surprised.

'Absolutely. Seeing your pretty face and reading what you've been doing on the news blog have kept me going.'

'Oh Rory.' She kissed him. 'Thank God you came back to Lilacwell.'

'Yes, and for Adira talking some sense into you,' he replied pulling her into him.

Chapter 16

Fletcher was busy packing. His Highland fling wasn't for another couple of weeks, but there was nothing like being prepared in his book. Truth be told he was starting to get rather excited about his little jaunt and wanted it to come earlier. Even the thought of having to tolerate Ruby didn't deter him. She wasn't a bad old stick, he told himself. Ruby always had Lilly's interest at heart, ever the protective older sister, and if it made Lilly happy, then he was happy. In fact, Lilly's happiness had become of paramount importance to him, now more than ever. None of them were getting any younger and he more than most wanted to make up for lost time. It was Ruby who had informed Fletcher of her sister's devotion to him. Had he known deep down? Had he chosen to ignore it for all these years, whilst conveniently letting her housekeep The Laurels? Maybe his conscience had been pricked, but there was no denying his genuine fondness of a life-long friend he cared very much for. All he wanted was the best for Lilly, she truly deserved it.

He sat on the edge of the bed and peered into his open suitcase. Lots of jumpers, thick socks and thermals, he'd need them on the chilly Scottish glens. His silver hip flask and binoculars were already packed, as he hoped to spend some time exploring the wildlife whilst keeping warm with a hot toddy, and he rubbed his hands together remembering the whisky bar advertised on the hotel website. Hell, he was going to enjoy that. He'd even packed a kilt, which had been tucked at the back of his wardrobe for an age. He chuckled at the memory of its last outing, some relative's wedding he'd attended years ago. Still, he thought, if you have the legs... as he recalled, he'd had many a compliment wearing that kilt.

There was a tap at the door. Lilly peeped her head round.

'Packing already, Fletcher?'

'Aye lass, thought I'd make a start.'

'Oh Fletcher, I've not a clue what to take. All that grandeur, I'm not sure my clothes will cut muster.'

Fletcher eyed her thoughtfully. 'What do you mean, Lilly?'

'Well... the hotel looks so posh and I'm...'

'What?'

'Not posh.'

'You're grand, Lilly,' Fletcher replied, folding his arms.

'But I want to look the part and I'm not sure I will.'

He observed her anxious face, almost like a lost child, and swallowed. 'Now just you listen here. Me and you are going shopping and I'm going to buy you—'

'No, I couldn't possibly,' she cut in.

'Oh yes, you can,' he replied with force. 'We are going shopping, getting you some new clobber.'

'Really?'

'Absolutely,' he nodded. 'I'll have you looking the part all right.'

'Oh, Fletcher.' She sat next to him on the bed, almost tearful. Where would she be without this kind, gentle giant? He was her rock, her support. Since she was a little girl, she'd relied on Fletcher, the older boy who looked out for her, whether it be holding her hand walking into school, lifts as teenagers in his open-top motor, sorting any DIY needed in her cottage, sending his gardener to cut the grass, the list was endless. And now he was taking her on holiday, with Ruby, and buying her new clothes. She looked down at her slippers, unable to speak.

'Just one thing though,' he whispered furtively.

'Yes?' Lilly's head shot up.

'Not a word to your sister,' he laughed, tapping his nose.

Lilly broke into a sheepish smile. 'Not a word, I promise,' she giggled.

Chapter 17

'Oh, Gran, it's beautiful!' Adira's eyes shone at the dress hung neatly on the door frame. As promised, Edie had had her wedding gown cleaned and was enjoying the effect it was having on her granddaughter. 'Just look at the detail.' She moved closer, inspecting the ivory lace and intricate pearl beading along the v-neckline. It was knee length with sewn-in petticoat netting – a true vintage tea dress and it fitted the bill perfectly. 'It's exactly what I was after.' She turned to her gran, tears swelling.

'Oh don't,' Edie waved her hands in front of her face, 'or you'll set me off!' They both laughed and hugged each other. 'Now come on Adira, let's get it on you.' Edie pulled back and took a good look at her. How proud she was of this gorgeous young woman. She couldn't think of a better person to wear her beloved dress that she'd treasured for decades. 'I'm sure it'll bring you as much joy as it brought me.' Adira beamed back.

'It will. Right, let's get this little number on.' She reached up and unhooked the coat hanger, then took it upstairs. In Edie's bedroom was a full-length mirror, and Adira couldn't wait to see how the dress looked on her. Within minutes she'd carefully pulled the ivory lace over her body and gently pressed down the creases so the material lay smoothly on her frame. She gazed at her reflection. It was a perfect fit, as though it had indeed been tailored for her. 'Gran!' she called excitedly. Edie quickly sped up the stairs, eager to see.

'Adira!' she exclaimed. 'It fits like a glove.' She shook her head in wonder. 'To think I was as slim as you back in the day.'

'You still are,' retorted Adira, 'you look fabulous for—'

'An old biddie like me?' teased Edie.

'No, for a lady of mature years,' she corrected, smiling. Edie laughed.

'I hope Jasper knows how lucky he is,' she said, still admiring her granddaughter.

'He does. I remind him regularly,' Adira replied, laughing too. 'And so does Fletcher,' she added.

'Ah, Fletcher, he's quite a character, isn't he?'

'He certainly is.' She turned to look back in the mirror, delighted that the dress didn't need any alteration. It was meant to be, just like stumbling upon Lilacwell and then meeting Jasper. All her stars were aligned to this very moment.

Edie smiled to herself, guessing her granddaughter's thoughts. She too, was a big believer in fate. What had been the chances of Adira's campervan discovering the small, quaint village in Lancashire which transpired to have connections to her father's family? Remarkable, really, and yet so *right* that it should happen that way. Maybe providence wasn't just coincidental, but a path determined to be travelled. She looked at Adira and in many ways was reminded of her younger self, full of life, adventure and optimism. And why not? Adira had everything to live for. Edie took strength from this, knowing how content her granddaughter was, a far cry from the exhausted, tense, pale-faced creature she'd witnessed months ago. Now her granddaughter looked fresh-faced and full of energy. Life in the countryside obviously suited her.

'How are the wedding plans coming along?'

'Good. I've booked the registrar, catering and flowers. Just to choose the music now.'

'What about the honeymoon?'

'Jasper is sorting that out.'

'Where are you going?'

'It's a surprise, apparently.' She gave a wary look. Edie chuckled.

'A romantic trip to Paris, perhaps?'

'More like a wet weekend in Wales. If I know Jasper, he won't want to be too far away from home or work.'

–

Jasper was in fact at The Cobbled Courtyard that very moment. Jessie had contacted him to say that she was moving from the living quarters above the pottery studio. She had had an offer accepted on a small bungalow near where her daughter lived in Yorkshire, so her retirement was imminent. Jasper had kindly offered to help pack her possessions for the delivery van that morning. It touched him to see all the tenants there helping out, too.

'It's a sad day for us all,' Max had told him. 'We've grown fond of Jessie. It won't be the same without her.'

'I'm really going to miss her,' Fitz agreed, looking a tad emotional. Jessie and he had been particularly close, often dining together in the evenings. He'd looked upon Jessie as a motherly figure. More than anything, there was a looming concern about the tenant replacing her. Would they fit in as well? The dynamics were about to change, leaving them all feeling a touch apprehensive. Jessie had laughed it off when hearing their comments regarding her replacement.

'Now don't be judgemental,' she told them with a wry smile. 'Never judge a book by its cover.' She playfully pointed a finger at Fitz, making him grin. Jasper once again was reminded of the close, little community of The Cobbled Courtyard — a stark contrast to the cut-throat world of business he'd come from. It made a refreshing change.

He, Max and Fitz had carried out the furniture Jessie was taking, while James bubble-wrapped all the ceramics left in the studio. Tom and Tess had provided everyone with hot drinks and bacon rolls mid-morning, which they all ate together at the cafe, one last get together.

'Well thank you all so much.' Jessie looked round her circle of friends. 'I shall miss you all dearly, but,' she nodded her head sagely, 'it's important to know when it's time to go.'

Jasper noticed Fitz's eyes fill. Max patted her shoulder, 'All the best,' he said, then turning to the small group, raised his coffee cup. 'To Jessie!' he saluted.

'To Jessie!' they all cheered.

After the delivery van had been packed tightly and Jessie had been collected by her daughter, Jasper went back into The Potter's Bolthole. He needed to take stock of what to replace for the new tenant. He wanted to advertise the flat as furnished; it would make matters a lot simpler than lugging about a tenant's furniture. He was glad Jessie had agreed to leave her kiln, he really would like another potter here, to keep the same feel of the already established business. Walking up the stairs to the flat, he noticed the dark marks on the walls left by the pictures Jessie had taken. He'd need to get the place freshly painted. Entering the living room, he decided to open the windows and get some clean air in. On doing so, he saw a picture frame face down behind the curtain. Frowning, he picked it up. It was a black and white photograph of a newly married couple, taken some time ago by the looks of it. The groom wore a pinstriped suit with large lapels. His hair was slicked back and he had a pencil moustache. The bride was very regal-looking, in a Princess Grace kind of way, with her blonde coiffured hair and timeless beauty. Then Jasper squinted to look closer. He noticed the same birthmark at the side of her cheekbone. It was definitely Jessie. Jasper tucked the frame under his arm to bring back with him. She'd obviously forgotten to take it. Then two thoughts suddenly struck him. He realised he didn't have a forwarding address to contact Jessie and secondly, why was the photograph face down? More to the point, how could Jessie forget her wedding picture? Surely it must be a cherished possession?

Chapter 18

'Very nice,' said the estate agent entering Rory's apartment. Her head moved animatedly round the room taking everything in. 'Oh and look at that view!' she exclaimed, walking to the bay window. 'A lovely communal garden, definitely a selling point.'

Rory didn't really have time or the inclination for small talk. He merely wanted to know the valuation. He had an idea after researching what neighbouring flats had recently sold for, but like the estate agent just confirmed, his had the added bonus of the garden. She turned to look at him and her forehead burrowed slightly. Rory guessed she was a similar age to him. He also assumed she was pretty keen to earn a decent commission out of him too, hence the overenthusiasm and coy smiles. Her head tilted to one side.

'Your face does seem familiar,' she said through slightly narrowed eyes, summing him up.

Here we go, thought Rory.

'Does it?' he gave a tight smile.

'Yes.' She blushed a little self-consciously, realising she may have come across as a touch too friendly. But since opening his door to her, something about his face had definitely resonated. She looked down at the clipboard containing her notes and read his name again. Rory Molloy, even the name sounded familiar.

'So,' interrupted Rory, eager to press on, 'what are we looking at?'

'Sorry?'

'How much is it worth?' He replied patiently.

'Oh, right, well I'll just take a look at the bedrooms...'

'Be my guest.' Rory tipped his head towards his bedroom door, then went to the kitchenette to put the kettle on. He didn't see the need to follow her in, it would only delay matters with further unnecessary chit-chat. Then he realised what a bad move he'd made by making himself a drink. Would it be rude not to offer her one? It might encourage even more conversation which he didn't want. He shook his head at how impatient he was becoming.

Since making the decision to sell up and leave London, he simply couldn't wait to go. Every day he talked to Cassie and without being able to touch her was killing him. And her too, he grinned roguishly to himself, judging by the fruity texts she sent him. Often he would throw his head back and howl at her naughty messages. They most certainly shared the same sense of humour. For the first time in his life, he knew he'd found his soul mate. Truth be told, he'd known it the second he'd met her. They'd clicked from the word go, almost as though they hadn't been strangers up until then, but old friends reuniting. Maybe that was the reason why it felt like they had known each other longer than they had. After all, look at what he'd done – quitted an extremely prosperous, lucrative career in London and was about to up sticks and move. Rory had always known he'd never settle in London forever, but Cassie had prompted the inevitable decision a whole lot sooner than he'd origin-ally anticipated. And now that he *had* made that ultimate decision, he was desperate to fulfil it and get the hell out of the city.

He yearned for fresh, clean country air, rolling green hills and a slower pace of life. He'd grown to hate the traffic, smog and crowds of London. He'd grown to hate the chambers he'd worked for and the bureaucracy of it all. Picturing Nigel Kerfoot's smug face made him cringe and want to punch him on the nose. As soon as he sold the flat, he'd be off. Workwise, he had fortunately completed the few cases he had had, not that there were many, as the activists had been his main priority, and now that had concluded. The construction company had taken over the whole site and all the climate protesters had been shifted. Their message had been heard, nationally, so job done for Rory. Realistically, the likelihood of the carriageway never being built was remote, but he hoped his efforts would bring the climate issue to the top of the agenda, instead of being batted away as purely an inconvenience, not to be taken seriously. Inadvertently, the whole saga had put him in a good position for whatever his next job might be – he'd made his mark in the legal world, and people knew him. Even this estate agent was going to recognise him any moment. As if on cue, she came back into the room.

'I know!' she beamed, pointing her finger. 'You're the Climate Warrior!'

Obviously she'd seen his wig and gown on top of the chest of drawers and made the connection to him being a barrister. Either that or she'd thought he may have rather fetish tendencies. He smirked to himself, then couldn't help but laugh out loud remembering one of Cassie's more risqué texts.

'I bet you get this all the time,' she grinned, thinking he was reacting to her.

He shrugged. 'Don't suppose it could be another selling point?' he asked with a bright smile.

'Hmm, maybe.' Her eyes ran up and down him. She gave another coquettish glance.

Oh hell, was she hitting on him? Whilst not wanting to appear arrogant, he really could do without this. His quick mind focused on the matter in hand.

'So, what would you put it on the market for?'

'I'd say in the region of seven hundred thousand to seven-fifty.'

He nodded; it was what he'd thought.

'Good,' he replied, then added, 'My girlfriend will be pleased.'

This earned him a cold stare.

'Right. I'll get back to the office,' she said in a clipped tone, arms crossed, clutching her clipboard. 'I can have it on the website by tomorrow,' she threw over her shoulder, barely looking at him.

'Thanks,' he said following her to the door.

'Bye, Mr Molloy.' She curtly tipped her head and left without another word.

–

'Thanks, Max. Yes, that would be great. Bye.' Cassie turned to Lisa on reception. 'The new curtain poles are ready. Max is coming with them this afternoon.'

'Will he be putting them up?' Lisa asked.

'Yes. He's also made the cast-iron fittings for them.' Cassie clicked on the hotel e-diary. It was just the superior, rear of house bedrooms overlooking the river that were getting the new poles, after having been recently refurbished. Fortunately three of them were empty that day. 'Normally Darren would help him, but it's his day off,' she explained. 'I'll give him a hand if needs be.'

Darren was the maintenance-cum-handy-man who was invaluable behind the scenes.

'The rooms he's decorated are gorgeous.' Lisa had loved the flamboyant floral-patterned wallpaper and bold colours chosen for the rooms. She would soon have to think of ideas for the baby's nursery. A warm tingling sensation spread through her as she instinctively stroked her growing bump. Cassie smiled.

'You feeling all right? Not too tired?' She'd noticed how much Lisa had grown over these past weeks.

'I'm fine.'

'Sure?'

'Yes, and thanks, Cassie, for giving me this opportunity.'

'My pleasure, you're doing brilliantly, Lisa. I'm impressed how well you've picked everything up.'

Lisa beamed. 'To be honest, I much prefer the admin side of things. In fact… I thought of maybe a few suggestions?' she tentatively asked.

Cassie looked interested. 'Yes?'

'What about putting more on the blog, like with the renovated rooms, before and after photographs, you know, just to keep people updated, that kind of thing?' She spoke quickly and with passion, which Cassie appreciated.

'That's a great idea,' she eagerly agreed. 'Let's start today, you could take a few pictures of Max putting up the curtain poles—'

'And the new fabric of the curtains, maybe say who made them, you know, advertise other businesses, then they could do the same for the inn.'

Cassie gaped at her. What talent had she tapped into?

'Lisa, that's a fantastic suggestion.'

A wide grin spread across her face. 'It's all about social media, Instagram, Facebook, Twitter, think hash-tags.'

'Absolutely,' Cassie nodded her head. 'And Max, we could mention him and his business, a local one at that.'

'Yes, then he in turn can mention us on his website.'

'Lisa, you're a genius.'

And to think this girl with such innovation had been busy scurrying round the hotel with a hoover and duster.

Later that afternoon Max arrived as planned. As his van pulled into the car park, Lisa was ready to meet him, along with a camera. He frowned in curiosity at Lisa taking a snapshot of the side of his vehicle. Getting the poles out of the back, he laughed as she squatted low to get a better angle of his van.

'What's this for?'

'Our blog. We're doing a piece on the newly furnished rooms.'

Max liked the sound of that. His van had his company name sprawled all over it. '*The Hot Spot*' in thick, black lettering, with a silhouette of a blacksmith hammering iron. Underneath was his website address. A picture of this on the inn's blog would do his business the world of good.

'That's great, thanks,' he said as he carried the poles to the entrance. Lisa quickly followed.

'We were thinking you might like to mention us on your website, you know, say who you've been supplying?'

'Yeah, course I will. Right, where are these going?'

Cassie appeared in the foyer.

'Hi, Max!'

'Hello gorgeous,' he smiled, making her eyes roll. Still the same old Max, forever the flatterer. She and Max had grown up together in Lilacwell and attended the same schools. They'd always been just friends, although Max had never disguised his attraction for her. Cassie knew his wild flirtation was harmless fun and aimed at many, so never took him seriously.

'Do you want a hand? Darren isn't here today and,' she turned to Lisa, 'we thought a few more promotion shots?'

'Fine by me. I'd have scrubbed up if I'd known.' He sent a cheeky wink their way, making Lisa giggle. Personally, she thought Max was looking pretty good with his slightly charcoaled skin and muscular arms bulging from his overalls. Hmm, very masculine; she snapped a few more discreet photos.

'Right, let's start in room twelve.' Cassie led the way down the corridor. Once inside, she climbed on a footstool and unhooked the curtains, while Max proceeded to unscrew the old rail. Lisa clicked away, making him chuckle. 'No laughing, Max,' Cassie told him, tongue in cheek. 'We want this to look professional.'

'Maybe get you in a shot? To add a touch of glamour?' he teased.

'Excellent idea,' said Lisa. 'Hands-on management, it'll look good.'

Cassie stood at the opposite end to Max. 'No, you look too wooden there, get closer,' encouraged Lisa, signalling with her hand to move in.

'Yeah, get closer,' said Max with a smirk.

Cassie moved next to Max, looking up and pointing, as if giving some form of input for the photo. She felt a little foolish, plus so small compared to him. Standing tall, his arms easily reached the top of the window frame.

'Can you just hold it here?' asked Max, needing to steady the pole as he reached for a nail in his pocket. Cassie squeezed in between his arms and reached up to grip. It was a tight squash, but between them they were managing.

'Well this is cosy, hmm?' whispered Max in her ear, as he screwed in the nails.

'All in a day's work,' she replied with humour, noticing Lisa capturing the moment on camera.

Soon the pole was up, ready to hang the new curtains.

'There you go.' Max stood back, making sure it was level.

Cassie admired the intricate twirls and twists of the cast iron, just like Jasper had. He really was a master craftsman.

'They're lovely,' said Lisa wistfully, wishing she had the same in her home.

'I'll show you to the next bedroom,' interrupted Cassie, wanting to move on.

'I don't suppose it's yours?' asked Max playfully.

'No, Max. It isn't,' replied Cassie flatly, ignoring his dramatic sigh.

Chapter 19

'Are you sure, Fletcher?' Lilly fretfully chewed her lip whilst moving sideways in front of the full-length mirror.

'It looks grand,' replied Fletcher firmly.

He was sat in the chair, kindly provided by the shop for patient husbands to sit and offer reassurance.

'But it's so expensive,' she said, still hesitating.

'Oh blow the price. If you like it, you're having it,' Fletcher told her in a no-nonsense manner, tinged with a touch of exasperation.

It was the end of a long, tiring day. Who knew shopping for clothes could be so exhausting? It was beyond him how women talked of 'retail therapy' as a form of pleasure. For him all this stopping, looking, trying on and agonising over an outfit was pure hell. Why they couldn't just nip in and buy the first thing that fit was past him. This had been the seventh shop they had visited. Thankfully, Lilly had liked most of what the assistants had selected for her when asked to intervene by Fletcher. Well, he'd no idea, had he? And Lilly fussed and faffed about far too much. Though it tickled him the way they had oohed and aahed at her, as she pulled back the changing room curtain and strutted out like a peacock. He enjoyed seeing Lilly's face light up when they had exclaimed how well she'd looked, using phrases like, '*The colour's just you!*' How can a colour *be* someone? Or, '*The waistline's so flattering.*' What was that all about? To him a dress either fit, or it didn't.

'Oh, I don't know, Fletcher, you've already bought so much. I'll leave it,' she said decisively, turning to go back in the fitting room.

'You'll do no such thing,' Fletcher wagged his finger at her. 'It's a smashing dress... the colour's... err...' he struggled to remember the words he'd heard.

'What?' Lilly searched his face, desperate for feedback. 'Is it wrong?' She looked down at the powder blue layered material. She'd always thought light blue suited her, brought out the pale blueness of her eyes.

'No! No, it's... it's... *you.*' There, he'd remembered just in time. He gave a nod to add confirmation. Lilly relaxed and smiled.

'Yes, I do like it, I must admit.'

'Well then, it's yours. Come on lass, they're waiting to close.' He tipped his head to signal the assistant hovering by the door.

'Goodness, look at the time!' Lilly hurried back into the fitting room, whilst Fletcher obediently waited outside to be handed the dress and pay for it.

Thank the Lord that was over, thought Fletcher, as he was passed the expensive looking carrier bag. He added it to the others neatly lined up on the floor. Good job he hadn't parked too far away with all this clobber to carry. Still, it had been worth it, seeing Lilly so happy with her new clothes. As she joined him, he bent down to pick them all up. On doing so he felt a sharp pain in his chest. He quickly straightened. Steadying himself he took a deep breath.

'Everything all right, sir?' asked the shop assistant looking concerned. Lilly hadn't noticed, she was too busy fastening her coat.

'Yes, yes, I'm fine,' Fletcher replied, waving his hand dismissively. 'Just had a big lunch, that's all,' he laughed. Yes, that's what it was, his body digesting the hearty steak and kidney pie he'd washed down with a pint of ale.

–

Adira was in the library sat at Jasper's desk. She had devised an itinerary for the wedding, to make sure all the timings co-ordinated. They were scheduled to have the ceremony at three p.m., followed by mini mince pies and mulled wine instead of canapés and bubbly, with photos at four p.m. The sit-down wedding breakfast was being served at five thirty by which time it would be dark. The firework display was to blast off at seven p.m. and then dancing until they dropped. All the guests would be staying at The Laurels, or in the shepherds huts on the glamping site, so they could relax and drink without worrying about driving.

Adira's excitement was building momentum. Next week would see the start of December. Lilacwell was beginning to dress for Christmas, with colourful lights decoratively illuminating the high street. All the artisan shops had gone to town with festive window displays and a huge fir tree had been hoisted up on the village green, ready to be switched on by a nominated member of the village. To her delight, Ruby had been asked to perform the honourable task this year.

Adira loved the community spirit of the village that Christmas brought, it was a new experience which she knew she would treasure in years to come. It also made her reconsider the guest list. Originally it had comprised of just immediate family, but now, having been made so welcome and a part of Lilacwell, Adira was having second thoughts. There were villagers who she'd like to include – Max, for one, as he'd been a big help to Jasper with The Cobbled Courtyard, and his granddad, Dickie. Plus there were all the other tenants: Fitz, James, Tom and Tess. Then she thought of Lisa, who was eternally grateful for the advice Adira had given her on pregnancy (whether it had helped or not). Each and every one had had some form of impact on hers and Jasper's life; it only seemed right and proper that they should be there to share their special day. She had to make the final decision on numbers as soon as possible, so would run it past Jasper that evening.

As she switched the computer off, she noticed a picture frame face down on the corner of Jasper's desk. She reached out to look at it. It was an old sepia photograph of a wedding couple. Who was it? she wondered. And what was it doing here? She studied their faces, the groom grinning widely into the camera, confidently poised with shoulders back, holding one arm round his new wife possessively. The bride radiated a classic beauty and gave a coy smile, but did it quite reach those mesmerising eyes. Adira was drawn to them, pulling her in, signalling… uncertainty? The photo intrigued her.

Just then Jasper entered the room. 'Jessie left that behind. I found it on her windowsill,' he explained, seeing her examining the picture.

'This is Jessie?' Adira asked in surprise.

'Yes, look.' He came to stand behind her and pointed to the birthmark by the bride's cheekbone. 'That's definitely Jessie.'

'Oh yeah,' said Adira peering closer, 'so it is.' Then frowned. 'Why would she leave her wedding photo?'

'I thought the very same.'

'Maybe she simply forgot to pack it?'

'Hmm, it was face down. Something tells me it was deliberately left.'

'Really?'

Deciding the picture deserved to be seen, she placed it on the middle shelf behind Jasper's desk. 'There, it seems a shame not to have it on show.'

'Even though they're no relation?' Jasper said half laughing at her sentiment.

Hearing Fletcher shut the front door in the hall, they expected him to come and join them with tales of his shopping spree with Lilly. Instead his footsteps could be heard climbing the stairs. Jasper called out to him.

'Fletcher! Good day with Lilly?'

'Grand! Off for a lie down,' he shouted back.

Adira and Jasper faced each other in puzzlement.

'He sounds tired,' said Adira.

'He's had a full day.' Jasper paused in thought. 'I sometimes forget just how old he actually is sometimes.'

'I know.' Adira nodded her head in agreement, a sad smile on her lips.

'I'll check on him later.'

Chapter 20

Rory closed the door of his apartment and checked his watch. He only had quarter of an hour before his next viewing. Since putting it on the market he had been inundated with prospective buyers. Rory hadn't thought his property would take too long to sell, having a desirable address in a decent location, but even he'd been surprised at the level of interest created. So far the estate agents had arranged seven viewings. He was finding it tiresome now showing total strangers round his home, intrusive almost. But, as he kept telling himself, it was a means to an end. Three offers had been made, but not quite the asking price, so Rory was holding out. He'd taken great pleasure in reporting back to Cassie on FaceTime in the evenings about how the viewings had gone. He made her laugh at his descriptions and impersonations of the varied people who'd looked round his flat. There'd been the tall, quiet, well-dressed man, who'd spoken in hushed tones and appeared rather anxious; Rory had him down as a politician buying a love nest for his mistress. Or the chic-looking thirty-something-year-old who reeked of expensive perfume, wore a smart suit and stilettos; she, according to Rory, was a high-class escort buying new headquarters. Or the couple with Brummie accents who sported designer tracksuits and heavy gold jewellery – they were drug barons, wanting to sink dirty money into property. Cassie had roared at his far-fetched assumptions and tall tales. She in turn, would give updates of the comings and goings of Lilacwell.

It wouldn't be long now before Adira and Jasper's wedding. Rory was so looking forward to being back there. He'd researched property in that area extensively and was amazed at what he'd be able to afford. Initially his search had been for fairly large houses with substantial gardens, but he soon realised that together with his savings, his budget would provide far more. It would allow him to buy farmhouses with outbuildings, renovated barns with spectacular views, or indeed land to build his own house. The possibilities were endless and to Rory, very exciting. His future could suddenly be taking a new turn. Not only would he be back home in Lancashire, but a whole new way of life was potentially on the horizon.

It had long been a dream of Rory's to live a simpler existence, firmly believing that less is more. His principals on saving the planet were real and now he could just have the opportunity to go the whole hog and truly commit to living an eco-friendly lifestyle. He had visions of owning a smallholding and becoming as self-sufficient as possible. Solar panels, wind turbines, even water wheels were his choice of energy supplies, rather than paying astronomical bills to gas and electricity companies destroying the planet. He warmed to the idea of keeping livestock and growing his own fruit and vegetables. The more he considered it, the stronger his aspiration became.

For the time being, he'd decided to keep his plans to himself and not share them with Cassie. Firstly, he needed to find his ideal property with the land he required. He knew she was avidly looking for houses in and around Lilacwell for him to consider. He didn't want to disappoint her if his needs took him outside her radius. Given the countryside surrounding the Trough of Bowland, it was highly likely he *would* find what he wanted, but he was reluctant to narrow his search too much. Secondly, he was a tad nervous at her reaction. How would she respond to his idea of living in such a, some might say, frugal way? It wouldn't be for everybody, he knew that. Would Cassie join him and embrace his lifestyle choice, or would she miss her creature comforts too much? He pictured the lavish surroundings of the Inn and Lilacwell and a nagging reservation itched at him. He recalled how she had looked at him in awe when talking passionately about defending the climate activists, but it was one thing saying and another doing. Actions spoke louder than words and whilst he was prepared to go all out for the cause, was she? Was he expecting too much?

He chuckled to himself remembering the rerun he had watched of the seventies sit-com *The Good Life*, where Tom had persuaded his wife Barbara to pack in the everyday stresses of a conventional life and live a more organic existence, by becoming self-sufficient, smallholders themselves. Of course, the series depicted a romantic, humorous take on what essentially would be a hard, compromising commitment. But, Rory conceded, it would have its advantages. They would be their own bosses, answerable to only themselves. And didn't Cassie say she wanted that? To work for herself? He recalled her complaining at the restrictions her job brought, living and working at the inn. Well, having the freedom to live off your own land would put a stop to that. Yes, that's how he'd sell it to her, emphasise the sense of liberty they would benefit from. Not to mention the healthy diet of organically home-grown food, the space, fresh air and exercise they'd enjoy... ideal for a family.

Rory's mind, as always when fired up, was working at full pelt. He would focus on the upside, hammer home the positives and convince Cassie it was the way forward. He was approaching this like a court case. In his head he had all the arguments for and was preparing answers for any line of reasoning. Then he forced himself to stop and take stock. This *wasn't* a case to be defended in court. It was his and Cassie's future that was at stake here. As a human rights barrister, he couldn't help but smile wryly to himself at how he was trying to steer Cassie's decision. No, she had to make her own choices. He would tell her how he felt and what he wanted, then let her make up her own mind.

Out of habit, he tapped on his laptop to open up the Inn at Lilacwell's website. Ah, there she was smiling up at him. He automatically clicked on the blog page to see what had been happening. His eyes immediately homed in on the new photos that had recently been uploaded. Pictures of a van with The Hot Spot logo on it made Rory read on. Apparently, a local blacksmith had been at the hotel to fit new curtain poles. He leant forward with more interest at seeing further photos of him with Cassie, looking a bit too bloody familiar for his liking. Instinctively, he searched for The Hot Spot's website to learn more about this Max-the-local-blacksmith. He scoffed at the page, which showed Max wearing a bandana and vest, hammering iron in his forge. It was obviously a promotional shot, showcasing his muscular chest and bulky biceps, but it certainly did the job. Max epitomised pure masculinity, which wasn't lost on Rory. Oh bugger off, he thought with scorn, what an absolute poser. He clicked back to the photos of him with Cassie, particularly the shot where she was under his arms, Max leaning over her, giving him a good view of her cleavage. The cheeky bastard. Anger started to simmer inside him. Just then the doorbell rang. His next viewers had arrived. He quickly shut his laptop and went to answer. Hopefully an offer of the asking price would be imminent. The sooner he was in Lilacwell the better.

Cassie clapped her hands in glee. After solidly scouring through various property sites, she finally thought the right one had presented itself:

> The bright open-plan kitchen of this four-bedroom detached house is the main hub of a family home and is great for entertaining. A spacious triple-aspect lounge with French doors onto the garden provides a great place to relax. The handy ground floor study is ideal for those working from home. Upstairs, retreat to your main bedroom with dressing area and en suite. You'll also find three further double bedrooms to choose from and a family room.

Cassie loved the new build set on an estate recently constructed off a main country road on the outskirts of Lilacwell. Location-wise, it was ideal. Rory had given a rough indication of his budget, so she knew the price bracket for her search. Granted, it was rather roomy for just him, but if he could afford it why not? It would save him from having to move in future, she reasoned, quite liking the idea of having a dressing room and en suite. It was naturally assumed between the two of them that they would be living together sooner rather than later. Despite having only known him for a relatively short while, moving in together didn't worry her, it just felt *right* and she knew Rory shared the same feelings. They spoke every day without fail and Cassie couldn't wait for him to come back to Lilacwell. She also knew it wouldn't be long before his flat sold, judging from the amount of interest it had generated.

At times, Cassie had to pinch herself she was so happy. Not that she'd been particularly unhappy before meeting Rory – far from it, Cassie was a confident young woman – but ultimately she had maintained one criterion; any future partner must be prepared to live in Lilacwell, and this had limited her dating options somewhat. She could not envisage living anywhere else and for her it was non-negotiable. So, to have found Rory who was the ideal man and also wanted to live in the same place was the perfect dream.

Her eyes scanned the immaculate, contemporary kitchen with white gloss units and granite worktops. The bathrooms too were done to a high spec, with free-standing baths, walk-in power showers, chrome fittings and black marble tiles. The garden was large with amazing views of the fells. It was superb. It ticked all the boxes. Well, it certainly ticked all of *her* boxes and she was bursting to show it Rory.

Cassie's imagination was reaching fever pitch as she pictured her and Rory making this beautiful house their future home. She imagined them choosing the decor and furnishings, really putting their stamp on the place. She sat back and pondered: probably they would go for the minimal but comfortable look, in keeping with the new build. Then, in typical Cassie fashion, she fast forwarded a few years and saw a cherub baby sleeping peacefully in one of the smaller bedrooms that would make a good nursery. And the garden, that too gave plenty of space for children to run and play in. Then she laughed out loud, maybe she was getting a little too carried away. As if on cue, Rory's name appeared on her phone to FaceTime.

'Hi, Pixie,' he smiled when she answered.

'Rory, I've seen the most fantastic house!' she exclaimed, straight in, without hesitation. Rory stalled momentarily, but it was unnoticed by Cassie who was in full flow. Without waiting for a response, she gushed on. 'You must have a look,' she said, eyes shining with joy. 'I'll send you the link.'

'OK, I'll take a look after. How's things?'

'Should I book a viewing?' Cassie ploughed on, not willing to change the subject.

'Err... well, I was actually going to tell you I've received another offer on the flat.'

'And?' Cassie was all ears now and had his full attention.

He broke into a huge beam, 'It was the asking price. I've sold it.'

'Rory! That's fabulous!'

'It is. It also means I can come up in a couple of days, once I've dealt with the estate agents and solicitors. No more viewers to show round.'

That was a relief in itself. He was more than ready for a trip back up north, more than ready to grab hold of Cassie. How he ached for her.

'Right, I'll definitely book a viewing then,' she said, face lit up with enthusiasm. How could he refuse?

'OK.' Then he added with a sly grin, 'Any room in your hotel, or are you fully booked?'

Her eyebrows rose and a sexy smile followed.

'I'm sure I can squeeze you in somewhere.'

'Good.'

'Rory?'

'Yep?'

'Will you look at the house now?'

Hell, she was like a dog with a bone. It sounded like she'd already set her heart on it, which started to give him a sinking feeling.

'Will do,' he nodded his head.

'And Rory?'

'Yes?'

'I can't wait to see you,' she blew him a kiss.

'You too, Pixie,' he winked back.

–

Later that evening he dutifully opened the link Cassie had sent. A dull, depressing sensation hit him as soon as he saw it. The house was the complete antithesis of what he wanted. A new, modern, soulless structure, totally lacking in character, sitting amongst other identical modern, soulless boxes, hemmed in with ghastly picket fences. Even the name of the estate made him cringe, *Bowland Rise*. A typical souped-up name, given to building projects coining in on the natural surrounding it was blighting, like blots on the landscape. He gave a heavy sigh. This was going to be far harder than anticipated, if this is what Cassie had in mind. That nagging doubt started to itch again.

Chapter 21

'So, you're all packed and ready to go, Fletcher?' asked Adira, smothering a giggle at how excited he looked, like a child on a school trip.

'I certainly am.' He plonked his suitcase down in the hall and looked at the clock. 'They should be here in the taxi any time now.'

'You've got your mobile phone?' Jasper checked.

'No!' Fletcher hurried into the library where he'd left it charging. He unplugged it and looked at the framed photograph on the shelf behind Jasper's desk. Where had that come from? He peered closer, vaguely recognising the groom. Then he heard the taxi honking and quickly returned to the hall.

'They're here!' called Adira, just as he came back.

'Yes, yes, I know,' said Fletcher checking his pockets and looking round. 'Right, there's nothing else I've forgotten is there?'

'Wallet?' Jasper snorted. 'You're going to need it.'

Fletcher gave him a shrewd look.

'I know that,' he replied, making Adira smile wryly.

'Come on then, we'll see you off.' Jasper picked up the suitcase.

Adira couldn't help but chuckle at seeing Lilly and Ruby sat in the back of the taxi waving vigorously. How sweet, she thought, hoping they'd all get along well over the next few days.

The taxi driver opened the boot to put Fletcher's case in, while Jasper opened the passenger door. As Fletcher climbed in, he suddenly remembered to ask.

'Oh, by the way, where's that photograph come from in the library, Jasper?'

'Jessie left it and Adira thought it was a shame not to display it.'

'Ready?' prompted the driver.

'Aye, let's get going,' replied Fletcher, then turned to the twins in the back. 'Ready, ladies?'

'Yes!' they squealed.

Jasper grinned. 'Have a lovely time,' he said closing the door.

Adira gave them a cheery wave and off they went.

'I do hope they all enjoy their Scottish adventure,' she said as Jasper came to stand next to her.

'So do I. The place will seem quiet without him.' He put an arm round her shoulders and she leaned into him.

'Yes, but it'll give us chance to get the last-minute arrangements ready for the wedding,' Adira told him. Whilst pretty much covering everything, she wanted peace and quiet to decorate The Laurels exactly how she wanted, without Fletcher or Lilly's 'help'. The Christmas tree was due to be delivered that afternoon and she was keen to get it in place, then dress it with the new decorations she'd bought. All the colours tied in nicely with her Christmas wedding theme of traditional red, gold and green. She'd collected holly, ivy, mistletoe, berries and pinecones from the estate and had got the estate manager to drop off some rustic logs. She'd bought red and gold pillar candles, scented with cinnamon, and hurricane lamps, all to add a cosy, soft winter glow.

Adira was eager to get started and was secretly glad to have the house to herself.

'I'll miss him,' Jasper looked wistfully at the empty gravel driveway. For a moment he was reminded of Fletcher's age and how precious his time now was. But then, time had always been precious with Fletcher. He gulped back the emotion and mentally shook himself. Adira eyed him pensively.

'It's only for a few days,' she gently spoke.

Jasper nodded his head.

'I know, but—' He cut off and swallowed again.

Adira was perceptive enough to sense what he was thinking and didn't want him upset, especially with the run up to the wedding. She kissed his cheek.

'Come on, let's get the place looking magical for his return.'

Jasper smiled. 'He loves Christmas, always made it special for me as a boy.'

'Well then, we'll make this Christmas special for him,' she replied brightly, cheering him up.

'Let's,' he replied, giving her a squeeze.

—

Lilly gasped at the first sight of Glenrick Castle. The brochure hadn't done it justice. It was even more splendid in real life, with its battlements and pointed turrets set against the backdrop of purple-clad mountains.

'Oh, Fletcher, look,' she whimpered, nudging him. He leant forward to see out of the coach window.

'Aye, Boudicca made a good choice,' he said quietly with a surreptitious wink.

'Shush,' giggled Lilly, 'she'll hear you.'

'I doubt that,' he replied glancing over the seats to where Ruby sat fast asleep. 'She's been snoring and spluttering like an old boiler for the past hour.'

Lilly put her hand over her mouth to stop laughing. Just then, the tour guide's voice boomed down the microphone, causing Ruby to stir.

'Ladies and gentlemen, welcome to the Glenrick Castle hotel,' she announced with pride.

'About time,' Ruby muttered, rubbing her eyes.

'If you'd like to exit the coach, a drink is waiting for you in the great hall. And please, don't forget, dinner this evening will be served at seven. I hope you've all got your glad rags and dancing shoes ready!' she chirped with gusto.

'Glad rags indeed. Huh! Some of us can't afford such frivolities,' scorned Ruby, this time audibly for Lilly to hear. It wasn't lost on Fletcher as he saw Lilly chew nervously on her lip.

'Did you tell her about our shopping spree?' he whispered.

'She saw the carrier bags and delved inside them,' she hissed back. Fletcher rolled his eyes.

As they entered the castle, all three of them were in awe of its grandeur. High ceilings with spectacular chandeliers cast shadows down the grey, stone walls. Winding spiral staircases led to corridors hung with tapestries and deer antlers. Once inside their rooms, they were equally impressed at the sheer luxury. Spacious and individually designed, each boasted a king-size bed, coffee machine, robes, slippers and aromatic toiletries. Fletcher rubbed his hands in glee; this is the life, he thought. His mood lifted even more at seeing the mini bar in the corner of the room. He'd crack that open before unpacking. Why not?

'There, all done,' said Lilly as she closed the wardrobe door.

'Any room left for my old clothes?' asked Ruby flatly. Lilly chose to ignore the dig and went into the bathroom to leave her toiletry bag. She was rather looking forward to this evening's dinner and refused to let Ruby ruin it for her. After all, it was *her* recommendation that they were all here. And at Fletcher's expense, she reminded herself. Perhaps she should remind Ruby too, make her show some appreciation for once.

'Are you going to be long in there?' Ruby's voice blasted through the bathroom door.

'No dear, just a minute,' Lilly appeased.

'Good, because my bladder won't hold out much longer.'

It's not the only thing, thought Lilly, looking bleakly in the mirror.

Later that evening, after eating a full banquet, having drunk fine wines and danced (to Ruby's absolute horror) many highland jigs, Fletcher was absolutely exhausted. He bid his good nights and made for bed. Deciding to have just the one nightcap, he poured himself a whisky. As he lay on his bed, contemplating his eventful day, it suddenly came to him who the man in the photograph reminded him of. Ronnie Taylor. He pictured his greased back hair, pencil moustache and rather smug expression. Aye, that was him.

His mobile phone rang, interrupting his thoughts. Picking it up from his bedside table he saw it was Jasper, as expected.

'Hello there,' he answered.

'Hi, everything all right? How's the hotel?'

'It's grand, it really is, Jasper. You want to see the place, it's magnificent.'

'And how's the company?' Fletcher could hear the humour in his voice.

'Lilly's an angel,' he answered.

'And Ruby?'

'She's lightening up,' he chuckled, remembering her flushed cheeks at dinner as he plied her with wine. 'Keep the battleaxe well oiled, that's my strategy.'

Jasper laughed. 'You do that. I'll let you get some sleep.'

'Night, Jasper.'

As he climbed under the bedcovers his chest tightened once again. He paused, then lay still for a moment. Soon his breathing became slow and steady, sending him into a comfortable sleep.

Chapter 22

Rory was speeding round the country lanes with the wind flowing past him. It felt totally exhilarating, giving him an undefinable sense of freedom, and in many ways he *was* free. For the first time ever, he had full control of his life. He'd made one of the most important decisions ever in leaving his career behind in London. Now he was at a crossroads, waiting to make the next move. He wasn't daunted by the prospect, just liberated. At the back of his mind it still bothered him how Cassie would react to his plans, but for now he was simply pleased to be back in Lancashire. His parents had been shocked to hear his news, but very supportive nonetheless. If anything, they had been saddened to hear how unhappy their son was in London and, of course, they were delighted that he would be living back up north.

Rory had done his own research since speaking to Cassie and had a couple of viewings lined up. One was a farmhouse with a few acres of land, just two miles outside Lilacwell. The other was a large Victorian house, again with land, but was nudging further into Cumbria in the Lake District. Whilst this looked an idyllic setting, it was over a good hour's drive from Lilacwell and therefore well outside Cassie's radar. Rory hadn't told her about these properties yet, wanting to run them past her in person once they'd seen the dreaded house she was keen on.

He shuddered at the thought. Surely once Cassie saw the potential with his choices, she'd be persuaded to ditch the charmless monstrosity on the new housing estate? He prayed she would – their future happiness was hinging on it.

He notched the car up a gear on passing the sign for Lilacwell, putting his foot down on the accelerator, eager to see her. His car revved into action and bolted down the open lane. This was another thing he'd have to sacrifice, his sporty little number. Although fast and economical, it was totally impractical for the countryside. He'd have to trade it in for a Land Rover, which didn't bother him; he knew it made sense and he'd had his fun with the Audi, but now it was time to move on.

He pulled onto the front of the Inn at Lilacwell and parked up. Grabbing his case, he made his way to the entrance and into reception. With a smile to himself, he remembered the last time he'd checked in with a jittery Cassie. How things had changed. When giving his name to the receptionist, she gave a cheery smile.

'Ah, Rory, Cassie said to go straight up to her room.'

'OK, thanks,' he nodded and headed for the stairs. Reaching the eaves, he knocked on her door.

'Come in!' she called.

Rory opened it and his eyes widened, then a slow grin spread across his face. There stood Cassie, wearing a black, lacy negligee and a sexy smile. 'Well hello,' she said, raising an eyebrow, putting her hands on her hips. Rory dropped his case, strode over and grabbed hold of her.

'Come here, you little minx.'

Giggling in delight, Cassie wrapped her arms round his neck as he lifted and carried her to the nearby bed. Frantically yanking off his clothes, Rory then eased himself on top of her gloriously seductive body. 'You look amazing.' His eyes burned with passion before kissing her with fervour.

It was a while later, lying in bed together, before Cassie managed to gasp, 'Welcome back.' Rory laughed while taking huge, deep breaths.

'That's the warmest welcome I've ever had.'

He pushed his hair away from his face and lay next to her. Cassie automatically snuggled into his warm body.

'I've missed you,' she said, nuzzling into his chest.

'You too, Pixie.' He kissed the top of her head.

The long drive and the energetic lovemaking caught up with him and his eyes grew heavy and tired.

'You sleep,' whispered Cassie. 'We've a full day tomorrow.'

The last thought Rory had was of that bloody awful house he'd been cajoled into viewing, then he switched off and gave into slumber.

—

Cassie had ordered breakfast in bed the next day and was just laying the tray carefully on the duvet when Rory sat up and stretched, his stomach rumbling with hunger. The full English smelt delicious.

'This looks great, Cassie, thanks.'

'Eat up, you'll need your strength,' she teased, pouring them each a cup of tea.

'Do your needs know no bounds?' he smirked, making her laugh.

'I'm so excited to see this house.' She sat on the bed at his side buttering toast.

'Yeah, I gathered,' Rory said between munching. Probably best to say nothing, keep quiet and hope she didn't like it. Though he thought that might be a long shot; Cassie seemed to have already made her mind up.

'What did you think?' She looked expectantly at him.

'Sorry?' He was stalling for time.

'When you saw it on the website, what did you think?'

How to answer? *I thought it was possibly the most bland, characterless house you could have picked and would have to be dragged screaming and kicking to live anywhere near it.* Maybe not. He carried on chewing, a further delaying tactic.

'Well?' Cassie's eyes bored into him.

'I think we should have a good look round, not set our sights on the first house we see.'

'Oh yeah, I know, but still, it ticks a lot of boxes, doesn't it?'

No! It doesn't tick *any* of mine, he wanted to mutter, instead he gave a tight smile.

'Let's just keep an open mind, yeah?'

'Of course,' she smiled, a little too smugly for his liking. Did she think it was all tied up – a done deal? He sincerely hoped not, sensing their first row on the horizon. His quick brain clicked into gear. He needed to divert her attention and enrol her into his way of thinking, play on the strengths of his future plans and get her on board.

'Did you manage to get plenty of time off work?' he casually asked, whilst dipping his toast into egg yolk.

'Ah, well now you ask, not really. Only two days.' She looked a touch sheepish. Rory immediately picked up on this and used it to his advantage.

'That's a shame.' He pulled a sorrowful face. 'I was so looking forward to spending lots of time together.' He looked earnestly at her. This did the trick. Cassie shifted uncomfortably.

'I know, Rory, and I'm sorry, but—'

'I understand,' he cut in smoothly. 'Work commitments.'

'Yes, but—'

'No really, it's fine.' He gave a reassuring nod, but still maintained the sad look in his eyes.

'Oh Rory, I feel terrible, but it was really hard getting leave, especially at such short notice.'

'Hmm,' he sighed, 'I see what you meant.'

Cassie frowned. 'What?'

He sighed again, then threw in his killer punch.

'When you said you felt married to the job, living and working in the same place, forever on call.'

Cassie's face dropped, she stared into space, contemplating his words. Rory, knowing he'd struck a nerve, continued.

'It makes you feel like jacking it all in, doesn't it?'

She faced him, still frowning. 'Like you did?'

He gave a non-committal shrug. 'Just remember your comment on being your own boss.'

'And?' Cassie was observing him closely with narrowed eyes.

'I agree with you, that's all.' He looked directly at her with an innocent smile.

The pensive expression on her face told him he'd given her food for thought, mission accomplished. For now, anyway.

As the afternoon arrived, Cassie's fervour gained momentum, though, giving Rory that uneasy feeling again.

'There,' she pointed to the signpost. 'We've reached it.'

Sure enough 'Bowland Rise' stood before them, waiting to be viewed. Cassie couldn't get out of the car

'No. It isn't,' she snapped back, folding her arms. Then added, 'Did you see the way she was sizing you up?'

Rory faked a puzzled look.

'She was all over you like a rash!'

He let out the beginning of a laugh, then immediately turned it into a cough when seeing Cassie's furious face.

'I'm sure she was only doing her job,' he tried to appease.

'Huh.'

'So it's a definite no, then?' He gently asked, touching her lap.

'A definite no.'

Rory grinned to himself. Obviously Cassie's opinion had been influenced by the estate agent's actions and not the house itself, but so what? He felt like punching the air.

Chapter 23

In The Cobbled Courtyard, Adira was talking to Max and Fitz – more precisely, she was asking them to make her wedding favours.

'I thought of bottle openers for the men, in this design.' She passed Max a drawing of a cast-iron bottle opener, with a laurel-shaped leaf for the handle. 'And a cute door-stop for the ladies.' She passed Fitz a picture which had a little shepherds hut carved into a wooden block. She looked anxiously at them both. 'Do you think you can do it? I know it's short notice, but I really wanted them to be unique, with a connection to The Laurels.'

Fitz nodded. 'Yeah, no worries.'

What else was he going to say? She and Jasper were his landlords and he was also a guest at the wedding, he could hardly refuse, but was happy to help anyway.

Adira gave him the thumbs up then turned to Max.

'Go on then, seen as it's you,' he grinned.

'Oh, thanks, guys!' she gushed. Now she had to sort out the flowers with James.

Inside the florist, she breathed in the sweet fragrance of all the flora and foliage. Unlike Fitz and Max, James had been given plenty of notice. He'd offered many suggestions, but Adira had opted for traditional Christmas colours for the wedding.

'Here we are, dear.' James ushered her towards his counter where samples of what he'd ordered lay spread out. Adira marvelled at the red and snow-white poinsettias, roses, lilies and carnations, sprinkled with bright berries and glittery mistletoe.

'And this,' he said, lifting up a delicate white flower on an almost leafless branch, 'is Christmas honeysuckle.' He wafted it under her nose. 'See, it has the most exquisite fragrance.'

Adira breathed in the scent.

'Oh, that's lovely,' she said closing her eyes. She opened them to see James looking rather pleased with himself. 'James, they're going to look beautiful!'

'Yes, they certainly are. And may I just say how delighted I am to have received an invite.'

'My pleasure,' smiled Adira. 'I'm so pleased all The Cobbled Courtyard crew will be there.'

'My, my,' laughed James, 'is that what we are? The Cobbled Courtyard crew?'

—

Jasper was in a meeting with the estate manager, Colin, who also had received a wedding invitation. He couldn't help but notice the man's slight shocked reaction when handing over the envelope. Clearly Colin hadn't been expecting one, perhaps due to the rather rocky start they had had.

Jasper, when first arriving from Dubai, had taken exception to the way Colin had blatantly let the state of affairs slip on their estate. Tenants' rents had been stacking up in arrears, buildings left unkept and falling to pieces, land standing unused and barren, instead of reaping harvests. Jasper had been staggered to learn that Fletcher hadn't been consulted or even shown the accounts or any bookwork at all for that matter. He'd soon whipped both Colin and the estate into shape and, to Colin's credit, he really had stepped up to the mark and they had now established a good working relationship. Colin knew the consequences if he ever let things slide again. Gone were the days when he could casually pull the wool over Fletcher's eyes, not that Fletcher had ever questioned him, which was the very reason why he'd become so lapse; he'd just been left to his own devices. But not any more. Things were very different now that Jasper had taken over the reins so well, and in many ways, Colin respected him for it. A mutual regard had grown between the two men.

'Thanks, Jasper...' Colin didn't know what else to say, taking the invitation from him.

'You're part of The Laurels team, of course we want you there, Colin,' said Jasper firmly. 'Now then, let's look at the books.'

Colin had all the accounts ready for Jasper's perusal, confident he'd be happy with them. He, more than anyone, knew the thoroughness of Jasper's number crunching.

Jasper's eyes scanned up and down the columns, taking in every last detail. 'What's this?' he asked, pointing to an item marked 'labour and costs to agricultural barn'.

'The barn on the far west field needed attention. The gable end is collapsing,' Colin answered immediately. Jasper sighed and shook his head. Although the repair work was essential, it was a cost he begrudged paying. The far west field was on the very edge of the estate and hadn't been used for years. Truth be told, it was a piece of land which had been standing still with no purpose for too long. At one time it had been part of another adjacent farm they rented out, but that tenant had asked to reduce his land as he grew older and had no children to help or pass the farm on to. Jasper's mind was ticking over, astute businessman that he was.

'I see. Let's take a look at it, Colin.'

Together they set off down the fields until reaching the barn in question. It was huge, made of rough-hewn grey stone, which in places was indeed crumbling. The roof was caving in and the wooden doors had rotted and fallen off; it was a danger zone and needed either pulling down flat, or restoring in its entirety. To restore it would cost a lot of money, that was clear, but as Jasper assessed the damage, a kernel of an idea began to form in his head. Colin looked on, wondering what instruction he was about to receive.

'I want you to make an application for planning permission,' he told him. 'This would make an excellent barn conversion.' Colin stared for a moment taking in the information.

'But what about access?'

'We can easily build a dirt track to the main road. This whole field can go. We don't need it and the cost to upkeep the barn is a liability. Plus, think of how much this plot, along with planning permission, will fetch.'

With that Colin had to agree.

–

Sitting in the castle's infamous whisky bar, Fletcher had struck up friendly conversation with many of the visitors who had also come to sample the wares. One or two had asked what the relationship was between him and the 'dear old twins'.

'I've known them all my life,' he'd reply. 'We've grown up together.'

'Have they always been such good fun?' asked one elderly gentleman, who had taken quite a shine to Ruby. Alfred was a quietly spoken, genteel chap who had joined the party without a companion and clearly had his sights set on her. Ruby, being extremely flattered to receive such attention, had taken him under her wing. Definitely a case of opposites attracting but, to Fletcher and Lilly, an absolute blessing.

'Yes,' Fletcher replied, 'especially Lilly. Ruby has always been the more...' He struggled for words.

'Extrovert?' suggested Alfred.

'Err... yes, certainly the more dominant one.'

'Ah, yes.' Alfred gazed over in awe at Ruby sat nearby, making Fletcher smile to himself.

They had all enjoyed a busy day's excursion to the nearby town. After taking in the shops and sights, and relishing a cream tea, it was back to the hotel for another evening banquet. Fletcher was tired from all the walking, talking, eating and drinking. He couldn't manage any dancing tonight. Instead, he and the twins, together with Alfred decided to relax in the whisky bar.

Lilly was wearing her new pale blue dress and feeling upbeat. Everything was falling into place – Ruby had an admirer, making her sister happy, and when Ruby was happy, so was she. Normally Ruby would focus solely on Lilly, forever watching and guiding her every move. But now, Alfred was receiving Ruby's attention, leaving Lilly free to breathe a little more easily.

'Over here, Alfred!' was her cheery call, summoning him to her; and up he'd scuttle like a pet dog. It was rather endearing to watch. Lilly had never seen her twin sister so smitten. The transformation in her was astonishing; gone were the snide digs and exasperated sighs, now Ruby actually *smiled*. She *hummed*.

Whilst delighted that Ruby was in such a good place, it did leave Lilly a tad concerned about where she'd be once the holiday was over and they returned home. Would her sister revert back to her usual self? She so wanted Ruby to remain upbeat. It would be better for everyone.

'Try this one, Lilly.' Ruby shoved a tumbler of whisky in front of her. Lilly sipped it, but to her all the whiskies tasted the same. 'It's peatier, isn't it?'

'Yes. Very nice,' replied Lilly, struggling to keep a straight face against the burn of the alcohol down her throat.

'Over here, Alfred! Try this one!' trilled Ruby. Alfred dutifully scurried over and the two sampled the whisky together, muttering about notes and finishes. She lifted her head to the bar. 'Fletcher, you too!' she called. Fletcher remained seated. He had his back to them and didn't move. 'Oy, Fletcher!' Ruby shouted, making people turn. But still there was no movement from him.

Lilly frowned. Ruby tutted and strode over to him. 'Can you hear me, man?' She reached out to give him a shove. 'Wake up, Fletcher, come on.' Then her eyes widened as she saw him clutching his chest. 'Call an ambulance!' she thundered.

Lilly gasped, loud in the suddenly silent room. Then, the hotel staff clicked into action. The emergency services were contacted, the bar was cleared of people apart from Lilly and Ruby, and a first aid officer had managed to manoeuvre Fletcher onto the floor and into the recovery position. Very soon, although it felt like hours to Lilly, an ambulance arrived, sirens echoing through the glens and blue lights illuminating the castle walls as it reached its destination.

Within minutes, two paramedics had Fletcher strapped onto a stretcher and wheeled into the ambulance, to be whizzed to Casualty at breakneck speed.

It had all been a whirl of horror for Lilly, who was shaking and tearful. Ruby, as ever, was the tower of strength, although she had had to down another whisky for stamina. It had fairly knocked her seeing Fletcher like that. She put a comforting arm round her sister's shoulders.

'He'll be all right, Lilly,' she tried to reassure, hoping and praying her words would prove true. She hated seeing Lilly this way, so terribly distraught and upset. The hotel manager guided them back to his office. Once he had seated them down with a cup of tea, he gently asked a few questions.

'Do you have the contact number for his family?' he enquired with concern. Ruby gave him all the details he needed, whilst Lilly, still shaking and speechless, stared into space. The manager looked at the two vulnerable ladies and his heart went out to them. 'I'll arrange transport in the morning, if you wish to return home,' he told them, feeling it was the least he could do.

'Yes, thank you, that's very kind of you,' replied Ruby knowing Lilly was in no fit state to stay in Scotland.

'But what about Fletcher?' Lilly suddenly asked. 'We can't leave him.'

'He won't be on his own,' Ruby said. 'Jasper is going to be here.'

'I'm not going till I've seen Fletcher,' Lilly announced defiantly, crossing her arms. Then promptly started to cry again.

'Now don't worry, ladies,' reassured the manager. 'I'm sure once we've heard from the hospital, we'll be able to sort something out.' That was the best he could offer at the moment, given that Fletcher was in his eighties and had most likely suffered a heart attack. He was anxious to speak to this Jasper now before making any more promises. Fortunately Ruby intervened.

'Come on, Lilly, you need to get some rest. We've all had quite a shock.'

Lilly stood up on autopilot and allowed herself to be taken upstairs to bed. Meanwhile the manager made the dreaded call.

–

Jasper heard the phone ring. It was late, past midnight, and immediately his chest started to thump. He'd been about to climb the stairs to bed when the loud shrill of the landline phone reverberated round the hall. Grabbing it, he listened to the Scottish accent and his heart fell. Fletcher. Something had happened to Fletcher.

Adira had heard the phone too, plus the urgent conversation that followed. Frowning, she put on her dressing gown and made her way downstairs. She inhaled sharply at hearing the words 'hospital' and 'clutching his chest'. Jasper put the phone down, tears pouring down his face.

'Whatever's happened?'

'It's Fletcher... he's... he's in hospital, suspected heart attack,' he cried, as his shoulders shook uncontrollably.

'Oh, Jasper.' Adira went to hold him.

After briefly hugging, Jasper stepped back, wiped his tears and inhaled deeply.

'I need to ring the hospital, then I'm going.'

'What? Tonight?'

'Yes.'

Adira sat on the bottom stair and patiently waited for Jasper to make the call. Taking deep breaths, she calmed herself to listen. She gleaned that Fletcher had been rushed in with chest pain. They had stabilised him and he had undergone an electrocardiogram test. After a couple more queries from Jasper, he rang off and turned to her.

'He's stable and asleep at the moment.' His face was drained of colour.

'Jasper, let's both go first thing in the morning. You need to get some sleep before setting off.'

'There's no chance of me sleeping.' He ran a hand through his hair desperately. 'I'm going. I need to be there when he wakes up.'

Adira nodded, knowing that nothing would persuade him otherwise.

'Do you want me to come with you?' she asked in support.

'No. It's best if you stay here,' he said, then kissed her, 'but thanks.'

Adira pursed her lips, trying not to cry. She wanted to stay strong for him.

'Drive carefully, Jasper.' Her voice wobbled with emotion. With one last embrace he left.

Jasper drove through the night in turmoil. The hotel manager had kindly offered him a room, which he'd only used for a matter of hours before heading straight to the hospital as soon as possible. He hadn't brought Lilly with him but promised to go back for her once he'd sussed out what was happening with Fletcher first. The last thing he needed was Lilly fretting before knowing the full facts, and the poor woman looked dead on her feet as it was.

He was seen by a doctor who quietly took him to one side and explained the procedures which Fletcher had undergone. An ECG had tested his heart's rhythm and electrical activity. He'd also had blood tests, which showed that Fletcher actually suffered from angina, the cause of his pain. He reassured him that angina could be steadied and improved with medicine and rest. That, and a healthy lifestyle, obviously. Too right, thought Jasper, already planning to ban Fletcher from the drink's cabinet. The news came as a huge relief, but changes were most *definitely* going to be made back in Lilacwell, he swore to himself.

Walking down the hospital ward, Jasper forced himself to remain calm. Then he saw him, through the glass window in a separate room, lying in bed propped up by pillows. His eyes were shut. He looked so peaceful.

Jasper stopped in his tracks. Then, taking a deep, calming breath, gently knocked on the door and entered. Fletcher's eyelids flickered open at the disturbance.

'Jasper,' he croaked and held out his hand.

'Fletcher,' he gulped and hurried towards him. 'How are you feeling?' Jasper's eyes searched his face. Although pale, there was still a twinkle in his uncle's eye.

'Better.'

'You gave us all a shock.'

'Gave meself one.' He gave a wry smile. Typical Fletcher, to attempt humour even in a situation like this.

'It's angina. Did the doctors explain to you?' Jasper was worried that he may not have taken everything in.

'Yes, yes, I know.' Then he looked sheepishly at him. 'I think I may have overdone things.'

'Just a bit!' shot back Jasper. 'From now on, I'm taking over, Fletcher. I mean it. There's no more whisky—'

'But…' Fletcher tried to speak.

'No, listen,' Jasper interrupted with force. 'No alcohol and no more fry-ups. From now on it's a healthy balanced diet. Do you hear me?'

'Loud and clear,' replied Fletcher faintly. Visions of the hotel whisky bar slowly faded away into the distance. So much for his Highland fling.

Chapter 24

Rory sat back and took a sip of his coffee. It was late afternoon and he was basking in the bright winter sunshine on the hotel terrace. Cassie was busy working and he was once more studying the properties he was imminently due to view. After the other day's tricky experience at the Bowland Rise new house, Rory was even more cautious about opening up to Cassie with his ambition to run a smallholding. Especially as she had upped the ante by searching for similar houses. He just couldn't second guess her reaction, more so when seeing how much she loved her job here in this luxurious hotel. It was obvious that in spite of the commitment previously mentioned, she still flourished in the role as assistant manager. Would she show the same commitment to his plans? He knew he was procrastinating. Hell, his viewing of the house in the Lake District was tomorrow, and *still* he hadn't broached the subject. Angry with himself for being such a coward, he decided there and then to stop being such a spineless swine and just talk to her, no holds barred.

It wasn't in his nature to be this weak, but that only emphasised to him how much he so wanted to succeed with his ambition, but with Cassie by his side. Such a lot was hinging on her views. He knew he was on safer ground with the second property he was due to see at the end of the week because this farmhouse was very near to

Lilacwell, in the nearby village of Chipping, which was one huge box ticked for her. But Cumbria was pushing it, hence the delay in discussing it with Cassie. Putting all this aside, when he read about '*this large Victorian renovated house, with original architectural features built in 1868*' he was sorely tempted by its character. That and the '*bounteous fruit gardens where strawberries, blackcurrants, gooseberries and rhubarb are currently grown*', plus the '*acreage of woodland adding further greenery and privacy to the area, where daffodils, snowdrops, crocus and bluebells bloom as spring approaches and the local wildlife is abundant...*' Rory sighed at the idyllic lifestyle all this pictured. A far cry from the city and all its chaos.

He jumped when Cassie's voice suddenly interrupted his musings.

'I've been looking for you!' she called, walking down the terrace steps to join him. Rory quickly folded the property details away in his pocket. 'What are you doing out here?' she asked, sitting next to him.

'Just enjoying the scenery,' he smiled. It was indeed a beautiful sight; winter frost glittered on the tree branches and fields beyond, and the distant hills were capped with a dusting of snow. All was peaceful, except for the sound of the river rushing through the forest and the call of a wood pigeon through the sharp, clean air. Rory had never felt so much at home. He was reluctant to be shortly returning to London, albeit temporarily to sort out the move. He regarded it as an inconvenience. It *was* an inconvenience. He needed to be here, in Lancashire, getting on with the next stage in his life.

'Penny for them?' Cassie tilted her head pensively at him.

Rory looked her full in the face. Now was the time.

'Cassie, I need to speak to you.'

Her face fell. 'What?'

'It's about our future,' he said in a serious tone.

'You've been having second thoughts?' Her voice cracked.

'Not about us,' he quickly replied, hating how wounded she looked.

'Then what?' Her eyes filled with tears.

Rory grabbed both her hands, annoyed at himself for already upsetting her. 'Cassie, I'm viewing a house tomorrow.'

'But... I don't understand, why haven't you—'

'It's in Cumbria.'

'In Cumbria?' Her voice held surprise and confusion. She snatched her hands away from his hold.

'Yes, the Lake District,' he replied quietly.

'Well, you'll be paying a bloody premium there,' she retorted.

'And there's another I'm viewing in Chipping.'

She stared at him, jaw dropped. He gave her a few moments for the information to sink in.

'And why, can I ask, have you not thought to tell me this before?' The confusion was replaced with anger now. Pin pricks of rage glowed in her cheeks and her blazing eyes burnt into him.

'Because there's more to it, Cass,' he replied calmly, meeting her stare.

'More?' she squealed. 'Like what?'

He leant forward to touch her, but she pushed him back.

'Please, Cassie—'

'What the hell's going on, Rory?' She was on the verge of crying. He knew he had to act fast.

'Listen, I want to explain—' Just then, Lisa called from the top of the terrace.

'Cassie, you're needed at reception!'

Rory closed his eyes. This was exactly what he'd been at pains to avoid.

She got up to leave.

'Don't go, Cass. Just listen to me, please,' he pleaded urgently. She gave him a look of contempt mingled with hurt.

'I've got to go,' she said flatly. He got up to follow her, then reached out and took hold of her arm to stop her. She turned to face him with a hard glare.

'Cassie, we've got to talk.'

'Later, when I've finished working.'

'Let's have dinner out, away from this place.'

'OK,' she nodded, somewhat defeated, all the spark knocked out of her. Rory felt frustrated and helpless. He tried to touch her face, but she dodged his hand. 'Don't.' She walked up the steps and left him.

—

Cassie's mood hadn't lifted on returning from her shift. The silent atmosphere between them was palpable. Rory had booked a table in a restaurant, in the nearby town of Clitheroe, and was looking forward to having no distractions, as well as offloading everything to Cassie once and for all.

Once seated he ordered a bottle of wine immediately, hoping that would take the edge off her frostiness. He then took out the house specs for both properties; the Victorian house in Cumbria and the farmhouse in Chipping.

Despite herself, Cassie was curious. She'd had time to calm down a little, but still couldn't help feeling hurt.

Why hadn't Rory mentioned these houses before? Her eyes scanned the details before her. She had to admit, the Victorian property looked magnificent, with its pointed arch door surrounds and decorative ironwork, and the farmhouse, although looking like it needed a lot of work, clearly had great potential with its land and outbuildings. All this and yet Rory had kept it to himself. After absorbing all the information, she looked up at him. Luckily for Rory, the waiter came with the wine at this point. When he left, Rory poured her a generous glass before speaking.

'Cass, the reason why I've kept quiet about these is because it's not just a home I'm looking for.' She frowned, but didn't interrupt, just took a long gulp of wine and listened to him. 'It's a way of life.' Still, she sat in silence. 'I want land. I want to *work* the land, grow vegetables, fruit, keep livestock.' His eyes shone with passion as he built momentum. 'I want to go off-grid, be self-sufficient, have wind turbines, solar energy, live off natural resources.' Cassie blinked. On a bit of a roll, he continued. 'I want to appreciate nature, breathe fresh, clean air and have space to…' he gazed into her eyes, 'bring up a family.' There, he'd said it. All of it. A few second passed before she reacted.

'Why haven't you told me all this before?'

'I was scared you might not want the same. This is my dream, isn't it?' He shrugged almost in defeat, but still with hope and reached for his wine. He'd said enough, now he needed to know her thoughts.

'Well, it's a lot to take in.' She gave a faint smile.

'It is,' he nodded, but still looked expectantly at her. He needed more than that.

'And… I guess I need to think about it.'

He had hoped for a more positive response, but then of course he would. Rory was used to winning people over with his words. At least it wasn't an all out 'no'.

'But Cumbria? No, that's not for me.'

That'll teach him to underestimate her. Whilst she wasn't sure about the lifestyle, she was sure about the location. And he couldn't help but admire and respect her for it. He took hold of her hand and kissed it.

'OK. Cumbria's out. I'll cancel the viewing. But what about the farmhouse in Chipping?'

'Yes, that's a possibility,' she conceded. 'Although I suspect it needs a shedload of money spending on it.'

'But, it is a possibility?' he asked, giving her a coy smile.

'Maybe.'

'And you'll come with me to view it?' he pressed.

'Yes, of course.'

'Good,' he gave a huge beam.

'And Rory, no more secrets, OK?' She arched an eyebrow.

'No more secrets.' He clinked his glass with hers. Then a playful smile hovered over his lips. 'So who's this black-smith that appears on your blog?'

'Sorry?'

'The guy putting up the curtain poles? Who was looking down your top?' This time he arched his eyebrow mockingly.

'He was not!' she laughed.

'Hmm, looked a bit too familiar for my liking,' he said with humour.

'That's ridiculous,' she spluttered, still laughing, then added, 'Talking of too familiar, I noticed that estate agent give you her business card.' She tipped her head to one side, waiting for his response.

'Which I politely returned,' he batted back with a wry grin, relieved to have the old banter between them.

'Yes, you did,' she smiled. 'Now let's eat.'

Chapter 25

Adira was trying her best to stay cool, calm and collected. Like a swan gliding gracefully on the surface, however, her feet were paddling furiously underneath. The wedding was just one week away. Inside The Laurels was pandemonium. Decorations were still being erected and the colossal fir tree standing in the hall had yet to be dressed. Last-minute arrangements needed confirming and amongst all this kerfuffle was a very suppressed, frustrated Fletcher.

He had been given strict instructions to bed rest. Something which didn't come naturally to him. Fletcher was always on the go, busy doing something, seeing someone. Having to spend time sat up in bed with a newspaper for company didn't suit. He hated the isolation, constantly calling for Jasper or Adira to sit and chat to him, which they were happy to, but were also busy with all the wedding plans.

Lilly had been an absolute angel, reading his favourite Dick Francis novels to him and continually running up and down the stairs with cups of tea, but no cake. In fact, under 'new rules' there was to be no cake, no fry-ups and above all, no alcohol.

Was life worth living? thought Fletcher bleakly. Then he reminded himself of how fortunate he'd been. He had been given a wake-up call to address his lifestyle.

Again. Just a few months ago he had indeed started a new, healthy regime, under his doctor's orders, but somehow he'd lapsed into his old ways. And this was the result; an angina attack and bloody solitary confinement. It was his own fault and he would not take life for granted as he had. He was needed here at The Laurels. Jasper needed him. A wave of guilt hit when recalling his anxious face in the hospital. No, from now on, it was porridge for breakfast, salads for lunch and a wholesome dinner in the evening. Whisky was out… hmm, maybe the odd tipple now and then. Well, he had to keep body and soul together, didn't he?

'Adira!' he bellowed down the stairs. Adira, who was occupied decorating the Christmas tree, looked up in alarm.

'Fletcher, what are you doing out of bed?' she asked accusingly.

'Oh, let me come down for goodness' sake, this is ridiculous.'

She hesitated. 'But what would Jasper say?'

'Oh, blow Jasper. He isn't here, is he?'

Just then footsteps could be heard coming from the kitchen back door into the hall.

'Actually, Fletcher, yes I am here.' Jasper stood at the bottom of the stairs and folded his arms, staring up at Fletcher in exasperation.

'Come on, lad, I've had enough bed rest. I'm coming downstairs.'

'He does look to have a lot more colour in his cheeks,' whispered Adira. Jasper gave in.

'All right then, let me help you down.' Jasper climbed up the stairs and hooked his arm through Fletcher's. Together they slowly stepped down.

'What are you doing?' Fletcher asked him.

'I was just going to look at some paperwork for the estate.'

'I'll come with you.'

Jasper eased him into the chair next to his desk in the study. Fletcher's eyes darted round the room, glad for the change of scenery. Then they rested on Jessie's wedding picture on the shelf behind Jasper's desk. He pointed to it, remembering who the groom in the photograph reminded him of.

'He doesn't half look like Ronnie Taylor.'

Jasper frowned then looked at the photograph too.

'Who's Ronnie Taylor?'

Fletcher laughed. 'He was the Midlands' answer to the Kray brothers.'

'What?' Jasper laughed. He'd assumed Fletcher had known him personally and that Taylor had lived in Lilacwell.

'Look him up. He was a gang leader in Birmingham, in the seventies.'

Jasper was inquisitive. He switched his laptop on and searched the name Ronnie Taylor. An image of him came up, making Jasper catch his breath. Sure enough, the exact profile of Jessie's husband was staring up at him from his screen; the slicked-back hair, pencil moustache and self-assured smirk. Jasper read the blurb on the page.

Ronnie Taylor was the foremost perpet-
rator of organised crime in the mid-seventies.
With his gang, known as The Circle, he was
involved in murder, armed robbery, protection rackets and assaults. He was sentenced
to life imprisonment in 1979 and remained

in prison until his death of a heart attack in 1985, leaving one daughter and widow.

Jasper's eyes scanned more images of him; they widened when they saw a family portrait of him with his wife and daughter. He clicked on it to enlarge the photo shot. It was Jessie, she had the same identical birthmark at the side of her cheekbone.

'Fletcher, you're right. It is Ronnie Taylor.'

Fletcher's head whipped up, he'd been browsing through the paperwork on Jasper's desk.

'Is it?'

'Yes, look.' Jasper turned the laptop to show him.

'Well, I'll be blowed!'

Both men looked at one another. Just then Adira came into the room.

'Coffee, anyone?'

'Look at this, Adira,' Jasper pointed to the screen. Adira bent down to see, paused, then looked at the photograph on the shelf behind her.

'It's him,' she said in amazement. 'It's Jessie's husband!' Then she, too, read all about the Birmingham criminal. She faced Jasper in shock. 'I can't believe it. Fancy Jessie being married to a gangster.' Her mouth gaped open in astonishment.

'She obviously didn't use her married name,' said Jasper. 'We knew her as Jessie Carter, not Taylor.'

'Don't blame her,' sniffed Adira. 'Who'd want to be associated with a murderer?'

'No wonder she left her wedding picture behind,' said Fletcher, then added, 'But why leave it out to be found?'

'Maybe she simply forgot to pick it up?' replied Adira, then out of morbid curiosity asked, 'Who did he murder?'

'According to this, it was during an armed robbery of a bank, where the manager was shot in the chest,' read Jasper.

All three of them sat in stunned silence for a few moments.

'And to think his wife lived here in Lilacwell, all this time, hiding such a secret,' remarked Adira incredulously.

'Ah well, there's many a country village hiding secrets,' said Fletcher rather sagely. Jasper and Adira exchanged a knowing smile. 'Anyway,' he clapped his hands, 'what about your stag do, Jasper?'

'What stag do?'

'Exactly. I'm organising one. No, hear me out.' He saw the beginnings of a refusal. 'Just a get together at the inn, to mark the occasion. I thought of inviting old Dickie and Max—'

'What about Fitz, James and Tom too?' interrupted Adira, wanting to include all of The Cobbled Courtyard crew.

'Good idea,' agreed Fletcher.

'You could ask Rory, too,' she suggested.

'The more the merrier,' cheered Fletcher.

'Don't I get a say?' asked Jasper flatly, making Adira chuckle.

'We'll have to be snappy about it,' continued Fletcher, ignoring Jasper. 'The wedding's next week.' Then he turned to Adira, 'And what about you? Aren't you having a hen do, lass?'

'Of sorts. Me, Cassie and Lisa are going to Clitheroe for a night out.'

'Good,' nodded Fletcher, then asked, 'Why don't you invite Lilly and Ruby?'

Jasper smothered a laugh and looked directly at her.

'Err… well, yes, I suppose I could—'

'That's settled then,' cut in Fletcher forcefully.

Yes, the old boy was certainly back on track, thought Jasper fondly. It had crossed his mind that the wedding ought to be postponed; but no, you can't keep a good man down. All the same, he was at pains to ensure Fletcher adhered to his new healthy regime. Unbeknown to him, Jasper had put a lock on the drinks cabinet. There'd be no more sneaky snifters. He had also binned his cigars and hidden the biscuit tin. Jasper was awaiting the outcry from Fletcher once all this became apparent. He was touched that Fletcher had wanted to organise a stag do for him. It would be good for them all, a bonding session. He still had to stifle his laughter at the thought of Lilly and Ruby out on the tiles with Adira though.

Chapter 26

Rory and Cassie pulled into the farmyard, immediately struck by the sheer amount of surrounding land. Acres of lush green fields and woodland wrapped round the old stone farmhouse. It was a promising start. However, on closer inspection, it was evident how much renovation work was needed. Rotten window frames, cracked glass and peeling paintwork didn't enhance the appearance of the house. The sizeable cracks in the stonework and dipping roof with missing tiles also hinted at subsidence. Rory's heart sank. Whilst he had a healthy budget, he doubted it would stretch far enough to buy and fully restore this property along with the outbuildings which looked to be in similar shape. Nevertheless, the land was perfect, giving him loads of space to grow plentiful crops and for future children to roam free.

They were greeted by a middle-aged man from the estate agents, who struggled to open the front door. With a mighty shove, it creaked ajar to reveal a rather dismal looking kitchen which smelt of damp. Cassie looked warily at Rory. Filled with disappointment, Rory took in the old wooden units, chipped tiles, filthy stone floor and greasy work surfaces. There was a rusty metal sink with dripping taps and a draining board holding cracked crockery. Dead flies mounted up on the windowsill and a fridge stood with its door open, displaying shelves covered in mould. The estate agent cleared his throat.

'Yes, the house hasn't been lived in for some time,' he said by way of explanation for its sorry state.

That's an understatement, thought Rory. The place looked like it had been derelict for years. When exactly had the photographs on the house specs been taken? Although the farmhouse had looked somewhat old-fashioned, the camera had done a sterling job at disguising the condition of the property.

'But as you can see, it's got plenty of room and is most practical.' He opened the door of a pantry to reveal dirty shelving filled with aged packets of food, tins and rotten vegetables. Mice droppings dotted the floor and the stench was revolting. He quickly shut it and wiped his hand on his sleeve. 'Hmm, right, let's move on.' He ushered them into the hallway which was dark, only having a tiny window, into the living room. An old, tiled fireplace covered with black soot stood in the centre of the far wall and a threadbare carpet with a heavy pattern gave off a musty aroma. The walls were stained with damp and the wind whistled through the frail windows.

Cassie looked at Rory again and saw the regret in his face and her heart went out to him. It was as if his dream had been snatched away. A prickle of shame stung her. Should she have said no to the house in Cumbria? Was she being selfish?

The tour didn't improve. In fact, it got worse, if that was possible. The bedrooms were equally as bleak, with huge cracks in the walls, again signifying subsidence, but the bathroom was the ultimate low point with its stained avocado suite, peeled lino flooring and pink flowery tiles. The shower consisted of rubber fittings stuck on the bath taps, with a plastic tube running up the wall to a shower-head fixed on with a hook.

'With a little TLC, this place could be special,' said the estate agent unconvincingly. Personally, Cassie thought he had some nerve showing them round this property in such condition, and at the asking price. Blatantly they were exploiting the land available and the location. Rory must have been having similar thoughts.

'Given the money needed to renovate, are the owners willing to be flexible with the price at all?' he asked optim-istically. This was greeted with a shake of the agent's head.

'Very doubtful, given that they have turned down three previous offers.' Rory looked crestfallen. 'It's in the hands of the late farmer's children, it being their inheritance.'

Typical, thought Cassie, greedy offspring wanting to wrangle as much money from the sale of the family home, yet didn't see fit to clear it first, or make it look even half presentable.

'Is it worth looking outside, Rory?' she sensitively asked.

'Not really,' he sighed.

'Oh no, let me show you,' urged the agent. 'Now that you're here, it seems a shame not to.' His head turned from Rory to Cassie in hope. He, more than anyone, recog-nised this young couple's disappointment. This rambling, decrepit property had been on the market for some time now and he'd shown several people round it, all of whom had had the same reaction as these two. Still, he was eager to show them the outside, as this was the property's greatest asset. Rolling hills of countryside and woodland surrounded the farmhouse, with uninterrupted views of the fells and beyond. It really was most impressive. If he could get them to fall in love with the location, maybe they'd be tempted and see past the crumbling wreck of a house. It was worth a try.

'OK then, let's go,' said a reluctant Rory. Cassie kept quiet and followed the two of them out of the door and into the farmyard.

A dirty, cracked concrete floor led them to a small gate. Once opened they found themselves in open countryside, and Rory's eyes suddenly came alive. This was exactly what he had in mind, acres of fresh green pasture. There were several outbuildings to the far right of the field which looked like they might need a bit of attention, but certainly seemed plenty big enough.

'The woodland covers five acres,' the agent told them, 'and you have fishing rights to the river running through it,' he finished smugly. Rory's head turned sharply.

'Really?' He couldn't remember reading that in the specs.

'Oh yes,' he beamed back, glad he'd struck a chord, 'absolutely. You've even got your own little fishing boat, that the owners are going to leave.'

Hmm, and what state will that be in? thought Cassie dryly. Probably ridden with rot and full of holes. There was no way she'd ever be stepping foot in it, that's for sure. She looked sideways at Rory and to her dismay saw that he was now mustering up interest for the place. 'Let me show you the outbuildings,' continued the agent.

To be fair, these were in better shape than expected. Apart from them needing new corrugated roofs, but given the size of the buildings, these wouldn't come cheap.

'It's a pity the farmer didn't look after his house as well as his outbuildings,' remarked Cassie. She imagined some gruff farmer figure, tight-fisted with his money only being prepared to spend his brass on the bare essentials for the farm, such as his animals, not on such luxuries as his family home. Judging by the decor of the farmhouse, it probably hadn't had a penny spent on it since the seventies, whereas the outbuildings had clearly been maintained well, with their pointed stone walls, solid oak window frames and asphalt flooring. Even the guttering appeared to be new cast iron. Rory must have been having similar thoughts as a laugh escaped him.

'We could always move into one of these instead,' he joked. Even the estate agent couldn't help but hide a smile. Cassie giggled, glad to see Rory had at least seen the funny side of things. She hated seeing him so disheartened.

They walked back in silence. All the time Rory was sizing up the situation. When they reached their parked cars, he had one final attempt.

'So, the owners definitely won't budge on the asking price then?'

'I'm sorry, we've been given very strict instructions.'

'Then it's a no, but thank you for your time,' replied Rory firmly.

The agent nodded his head, fully understanding. He didn't see this dilapidated farmhouse shifting off the market any time soon. Not without a considerable drop in price at any rate. It was a shame really, when this young couple could pour so much love and life into the place and make it a family home again.

They drove back, thoroughly dejected. Cassie broke the silence.

'Do you want to view the house in Cumbria?'

'No, like you said, it's too far. We've both got to be happy, haven't we?'

'Something will turn up,' she said with hope.

'Yeah, it will,' he replied. It better had, and soon. He had to pack up all his possessions very soon and needed somewhere to store them. Plus he couldn't stop at the Inn indefinitely. He had to find somewhere to stay whilst looking for a home. Not to mention start earning a livelihood. All the time the clock was ticking.

Chapter 27

'How's your stag do coming along?' Adira asked, sat at her dressing table, putting on a necklace in preparation for her hen do that night. Jasper had bought it for her whilst still in Dubai. Unlike most of the bright gold jewellery that was sold out there, it was unusually made of deep blue and aquamarine glass gems.

Jasper looked at Adira's reflection in the mirror and admired the woman he was going to marry; her elegant neck, flawless skin, silky blonde hair running down her back and her sparkling blue eyes. The necklace complemented her colouring beautifully. He remembered buying it in the vast shopping mall, whilst missing her terribly. Little did he know then that he would shortly be taking her out there. Not that Adira knew any of this, but Jasper had planned a trip to Dubai for their honeymoon. He wanted her to experience the place where he had lived, longing to show her the long stretches of golden sand, the clear turquoise sea, the breathtaking buildings, the classy restaurants and cocktail bars; plus the old Dubai with its traditional souks, vibrantly trading gold, silk, perfumes and spices, where the heady fragrance of the exotic essential oils, oud and bakhoor fill the air. He felt sure she'd appreciate the culture and experience, being a keen traveller. He'd wanted to surprise her on their wedding day. All he had told her was to pack 'light clothes', that had been the only clue she had been allowed, much to her frustration. He had secretly bought her a few items of clothing, including beach wear, with the help of Cassie, who had been sworn to silence.

Adira looked quizzically at him when he still hadn't answered her question.

'Stag do?' she prompted.

'Oh, yeah, Fletcher's sorted it. Thursday's the best night for everyone. Not the night before the wedding as he'd originally planned.' Jasper rolled his eyes. He could just imagine Fletcher forcing drink down them all, giving them whacking hangovers for the next morning. Adira chuckled.

'He's never really grown up, has he?' she said with amusement.

'No. But he's in for a shock if he thinks he'll be knocking back the whisky.'

'Hmm, go easy on him.'

Jasper gave her a reproachful look.

'Fletcher doesn't do easy. You have to be firm with him. God knows what he's got up his sleeve as best man.'

Adira started to giggle, then quickly glanced at her watch.

'Better get going, they'll be wondering where I am.' Adira had booked a table in the Italian restaurant that Jasper had first took her to in Clitheroe, which held senti- mental value as well as having an excellent reputation.

'Come on then, your carriage awaits.'

Jasper was picking up Lilly and Ruby and taking them all into Clitheroe, whilst Cassie and Lisa were getting a lift from Rory. While she had had reservations on inviting Lilly and Ruby to her hen do, Cassie and Lisa had thought it was hilarious that they had accepted the invitation with relish, and Adira was looking forward to the evening. It had been a long time since she'd enjoyed a girls' night out. At university she had had a great social life, but afterwards, working as a barrister in a London chambers had given her little time for socialising. The Law Society dinners she'd had to endure had proven dull and boring, full of pompous wannabes, desperate to climb to the peak of their careers. How glad she was to put all that behind her. It felt like a lifetime ago now.

Lilly and Ruby were ready and waiting, evidently excited for the evening too. Lilly had chosen to wear her pale blue dress again, whilst Ruby had actually bought a new floral blouse and pleated skirt for the occasion. Both ladies had had a trip to the hairdresser's for a wash and set, and sported identical fixed waves.

'It's so good of you to take us,' thanked Lilly, climbing into the back seat.

'Yes, much appreciated,' said Ruby, then nudged her sister. 'Put your seat belt on Lilly.'

Off they set, with the twins constantly chatting all the way. Jasper joked and teased, warning them all to behave themselves, causing more giggles from the back seat. Adira smiled to herself.

Cassie and Lisa were already sat at the table in the restaurant and waved up at them as they entered. Cassie had decorated the table with balloons and put plastic tiaras on the place mats for each of them to wear. A bottle of champagne was cooling in an ice bucket. Lisa had opted for tonic water, but still sipped it from a flute glass.

'To Adira, happy hen do!' Cassie held up her glass and everyone joined in. Lilly and Ruby put each other's tiara on, checking they were straight and didn't flatten their new curls.

As the Italian music played, all the hens drank, ate, laughed and sang along, swaying from side to side.

'*As the moon hits the sky, like a big pizza pie—*'

'That's amore!' they all bellowed in unison, causing a few raised eyebrows and playful smiles from the waiters. As the song continued, the hens got louder and louder, totally oblivious to the rest of the diners. They were having a blast and didn't care who knew.

'*But you see back in old Napoli—*'

'That's amore-eee!' they roared the final words to the applause of the whole restaurant.

Meanwhile, back in The Laurels, Fletcher was rattling the drinks cabinet in an attempt to get at the whisky. Pulling harder at the handle, he realised it was in fact locked. Bugger. Jasper had obviously sealed it up. Slumping down into his chair, he sighed and closed his eyes. Is this what the rest of his life entailed? He enjoyed his pre-dinner (and after dinner) drinks. It was one of life's simple pleasures. The healthy diet he could just about adapt to. Porridge with a teaspoon of jam was actually quite nice and the lunches Lilly made with a variety of salads and fruits, or home-made soup packed with vegetables and crusty wholemeal bread, were very tasty. The evening meals too, were always nutritious. Adira had made them lots of fish dishes, or chicken, red meat only occasionally, and desserts the odd time. He hardly missed the egg, bacon, sausage, black pudding and fried bread, which he used to eat most mornings. Well, not *too* much, he conceded. It was just a case of mind over matter... but hell, he did miss his whisky. It was good for his circulation, he'd claimed to an unconvinced Jasper. 'So is exercise,' he had replied. 'Let's go for a gentle stroll.' Blow that, Fletcher had thought, he didn't want a bloody stroll, he wanted a whisky!

Then, in a flash, inspiration hit him. He had a few mini bottles of different whiskies that he'd bought at Glenrick Castle on holiday. They were still in his suitcase. Rubbing his hands together he quietly made for his bedroom, passing Jasper in the hall.

'Fletcher, dinner's almost ready.'

'Grand,' he smiled and started to climb the stairs. 'I won't be a minute,' he nonchalantly called over his shoulder, all the time his mouth buds watering at the thought of those whisky bottles tucked away in the pocket of his case.

He quickly opened his wardrobe, pulled out his suit-case and put it on the bed. Unzipping it, he felt at the pocket for the bottles. Nothing. They weren't there. Unbelievable – Jasper had obviously emptied his case. He'd been one step ahead of him. Damn!

Sloping back downstairs and into the dining room, Jasper was sat patiently waiting for him at the table.

'Tuck in, Fletcher,' he smiled, knowing full well what the old boy had been up to. 'Fresh salmon, jacket potato, salad and,' he pushed a carafe forward, 'water.'

'Lovely,' said a subdued Fletcher, 'bloody lovely.'

Chapter 28

When Rory's solicitor had rung to say the exchange was imminent and he had to sign all the relevant documents, it was with mixed feelings that he set off back to London. Though he was sad to be leaving Lilacwell, even temporarily, there was a thrill of excitement that kept rising at the knowledge that this was it for his city life, and the start of his next chapter. His car was filled with empty cardboard boxes which Cassie had collected from the hotel's wine deliveries. At least he could make a start in packing up the stuff in his flat, though he'd need to hire a van to haul it all back to Lilacwell. He also planned to sell his car on returning to Lancashire and buy something bigger, more practical and cheaper to run.

It was a strange feeling when entering his flat, almost like it had never been his home. Perhaps it hadn't. What was the saying, home is where the heart is? And his heart was firmly in Lilacwell. His heart was also firmly fixed on Cassie. It seemed incredulous that having only known her a relatively short period of time, he had absolutely no doubts whatsoever that his future belonged with her. He loved her. It was that simple. As corny as it sounded, and Rory really wasn't that sentimental, he truly believed he had fallen for Cassie the moment he had clapped eyes on her. He suspected she felt similar, given the way she had acted in the same vein; just as sure and confident as he.

Never had she said, '*Don't be silly, Rory, we can't possibly live together so soon.*' No, on the contrary, she'd been as keen as he was. 'Runaway train' that's what his mother had often called him. Forever jumping on to one cause or another, full pelt, full throttle. Well, it looked like this runaway train had met his match.

Cassie, after much consideration, had grown accustomed to the idea of living a self-sufficient lifestyle. True, she did have reservations about quitting her job but, as ever, Cassie had had one or two plans of her own. Still wanting to stay connected to the hospitality industry, the idea of running guest accommodation really appealed to her. In exactly what format would have to be decided once their future home was bought. Ideally, Cassie wanted to renovate outbuildings into holiday lets, preferring to keep guests separate from their own home. Or, alternatively, if they ended up with a large house, then segregating rooms into a separate guest wing. This would provide further income for them, whilst still living and running a smallholding. Not that she planned to compete with The Laurels glamping site, but she was thinking of a different concept. It was the smallholding that was the pull, attracting a certain clientele that wanted a taste of the good life. She imagined sharing communal home-made dinners, cooked with their own fresh produce. Maybe her and Rory giving talks on their eco way of life to others who were contemplating starting up a smallholding, too. Even families who wanted to experience self-sufficient living might visit them. The more she considered the possibilities, the more enthusiastic she became. Which in turn made Rory a very happy man. Having Cassie fully on board, injecting her fizz and *joie de vivre* was just the tonic he needed. And, Cassie being Cassie, she had other ideas too. Taking Lisa's approach of advertising, or 'selling yourself', as she had with the inn's website, Cassie tried to persuade Rory to really milk the 'Climate Warrior' tag he'd been dubbed. Seeing the wary look he'd given her, only accelerated her argument.

'Just think, Rory, you could set up your own website as The Climate Warrior and blog about all the wonderful things we're going to do.' Rory still wasn't convinced. He really had hated all the media attention directed at him personally. The notion of creating even more didn't inspire him. Still, Cassie wouldn't relent. 'It could encourage others to do the same, live a simpler, sustainable life. You— no, *we* would be setting the example.'

Now there, she did have a point, he conceded. He rather warmed to the idea of the two of them appearing together on a website. He imagined the photos; working side by side on the land, digging vegetable patches, feeding chickens, chopping wood, harvesting the crops. Then on a more personal level; cosying up by campfires, cooking meals with their own fresh produce, maybe even future children – running carefree and barefoot in the fields…

He looked wistfully into the distance in contemplation. Cassie knew she'd struck the right nerve and ploughed on.

'We could even approach the radio, or TV and see if they'd be interested in covering our journey.' His eyes darted back to hers.

'What?' he asked beginning to feel uneasy again.

'Don't look so alarmed,' she laughed, then added with a sly grin, 'There could be money in it.' she raised an eyebrow. Rory gazed in awe of her. My God, she really was a force to be reckoned with. When she was in, she was *all* in. Now, who did that remind him of? he thought with irony.

'OK,' he'd nodded, 'let's give it some thought.'

So, on this occasion, his return to London wasn't a totally depressing one. It was merely a stepping stone to future prospects. Having a solid plan had given them both focus and impetus, and had also intensified their search to find a house with land as soon as possible. Time was of the essence; he had no job now and Cassie was ready to hand in her notice the moment they found the right property. It was both exciting and daunting in equal measure. Rory knew that both of them having a 'go-for-it' attitude had considerably sped things along. He doubted that he'd be in this position with any other woman. But then Cassie wasn't any other woman; she was unique in his eyes.

He'd recently met the parents on a visit to their farm. This had gone very well to his relief, remembering how previous girlfriends' parents had been. The clipped tones of, '*Elbows off the table, Rory*', from Sonya's mother, would remain with him forever. Cassie's parents were down to earth which, being farmers, he had expected. They'd talked for hours about crop rotation, cattle markets, harvesting and the lambing season, and he seemed to fit in seamlessly with the Wright family, so much so that he was looking forward to taking Cassie to meet his parents too.

Rory had been impressed with their farm and was surprised to learn that they were tenants of The Laurels estate. Cassie's dad had spoken very highly of Fletcher, and now Jasper. They in turn had been interested to learn more about his connections to Adira through Goldgate Chambers. He was eager for them to know he wasn't in any way an affected barrister, just an ordinary man, who happened to think the world of their daughter; and she of him. This had been blatantly visible from the moment they arrived hand in hand and the little loving touches they'd given each other throughout the day. Rory had never considered himself an overly affectionate man, but something about Cassie had him constantly reaching out to her, catching her hand or putting an arm round her waist.

Cassie's parents had instantly taken to this extremely polite young man with impeccable manners. Not at all like the jumped-up chap from London she'd once dated, who they'd secretly disliked. They'd been further delighted to learn of Cassie and Rory's plans, glad that they would be, if not in Lilacwell, then very nearby.

All in all, life was good for Rory. A far cry from the days when it was just work and sleep in a city full of anonymous people. He lined all the cardboard boxes up by the dining table, ready to start filling them. He was going to make a start that evening, finishing off tomorrow after he'd visited the solicitors and estate agents. Fortunately he had sold what little furniture he had along with the apartment, which meant he only had to clear his personal possessions. He went to his bedroom and saw his barrister's wig and gown on the chest of drawers. He didn't miss wearing them. Law had been a means to an end, a field in which he'd excelled, but nevertheless was glad to get out. His mind cast back to the dismal daily routine; up at five thirty to fight the city traffic, arrive at Goldgate Chambers, meet clients, attend court, back to the chambers, pick up more briefs, work into the early evening, back home for a tea in front of the TV, pore over more law, shower, bed. Only to start the whole process again the next morning. *How* had he managed to sustain it for so long? How long had it been since he'd met up with his mates from Lancaster? He'd stopped being invited for nights out and weekend stays after making so many excuses not to come up and see them. Although they had been genuine – he really couldn't afford to spend the time. He'd always had too much on workwise. How he regretted it now, though hopefully they would reconnect once he'd made the move. He'd been pleased to receive an invite to Jasper's stag do, albeit just drinks at the inn. Still, it would be good to get to know Jasper and the rest of the blokes. He saw it as an ideal opportunity, as a future resident of Lilacwell. He was looking forward to some male company.

Shaking himself, he opened the drawers and began emptying them. The sooner he cleared this flat, the sooner he could go.

–

Cassie was on a high. She was motivated and full of enthusiasm for what lay ahead, and having her parents' seal of approval with Rory had made her even more so. There was just *one* thing though that refused to disappear and lay dormant in the recess of her mind. A kernel of disappointment had started to take root. Whilst her feelings for Rory were genuine and she didn't doubt his commitment, it had niggled her that he had never mentioned marriage. Maybe she was being old-fashioned? After all, how many couples nowadays *did* marry before living together? But even so, the fact that he had talked about bringing up a family together must count for something, surely? Or did that simply not matter? Had it never occurred to him that she would want to be husband and wife? Because, actually, she did.

Cassie was a traditionalist. She craved stability. She was a creature of habit, hence her reluctance to move from

Lilacwell, her home village. She also liked to feel safe and secure in a relationship, hence her ditching the unreliable Justin. In Rory she had found all three qualities – stability, safety and security – and she knew Rory felt the same, why else would he be planning his future with her? So why not acknowledge this and commit fully?

Granted, they would have enough to contend with in finding the right property and possibly having to renovate it, plus start up the smallholding, but all the same, she did want to marry. It would seal everything together, make them complete in her eyes. Also, there was the legal side of things. Both of them were sinking their savings into the project and whilst Rory had far more to contribute, she still had a considerable sum to bring to the table. It was Rory himself who had insisted on them opening a joint bank account, and for both names to appear on the deeds of their future house. So why not get married? It made perfect sense, well to her it did.

Only having known each other months didn't deter her in the slightest. Look at her own parents – they had got engaged after a fortnight! And they had stood the test of time.

Adira had laughed when Cassie had voiced her thoughts, saying she was surprised Rory hadn't whisked her away to elope. She, more than most, knew how impetuous he could be, especially when setting his mind upon something. So, all things considered, *why* hadn't Rory popped the question? Then another thought suddenly occurred to Cassie, one which gave her food for thought. Her phone rang, and it was the very man FaceTiming her. She smiled at seeing his face.

'Hi, Pixie.'

'Hi. Busy?' she could make out all the boxes behind him piled up, ready to be transported back to Lancashire.

'Yeah, nearly finished now, though. I've hired a man with a van to come back with me tomorrow.' Fortunately, Cassie's dad had offered him a barn to use as storage space.

'Good. I'm looking forward to seeing you.' She blew him a kiss.

'Hmm, should I expect the same welcome as last time?' he asked with a wink.

'You never know your luck.'

'Oh, I do. I'm a very lucky man,' he said, looking straight at her.

So why not ask me to marry you? she thought.

'Cass?' he looked quizzically at her.

'Yes?'

'You all right?'

'Yes of course.' She forced a smile.

'What's up?' He narrowed his eyes, sensing something was afoot.

'Nothing,' she laughed. 'What time will you be back tomorrow?'

'Early afternoon hopefully. I'm aiming to set off first thing in the morning.'

'Have a safe trip.' She blew him another kiss.

'OK, see you tomorrow.' He mouthed a kiss back.

What was the matter with her? He most definitely caught some negative vibe there. He frowned, wondering what it could be. The one thing Rory hated was being left in the dark. He was tempted to ring her back and get to the bottom of it. No. He'd have a better idea tomorrow when he saw her in the flesh.

Cassie had given the manager of the hotel notice of her intention to leave. Outlining her and Rory's plans, she had informed him that once the right property and land had been obtained, her energies would be poured into that. He'd been taken aback initially, but couldn't fail to be both astonished and yet have admiration for her proposed new way of life.

'It'll be a lot different to living here,' he half joked.

'I know,' Cassie agreed, 'but more rewarding, I hope.'

To that he shook her hand and smiled. 'Well, the best of luck to you, Cass. You deserve it.'

'Thanks.'

'But what am I going to do without my number one assistant manager?'

Cassie had indeed given the matter some thought. A name did spring to mind, but she suspected the timing could be wrong. Lisa. To her, Lisa had shown such promise in her new role and fully believed in her potential. Lisa was keen to learn, reliable, capable and trustworthy. She was also pregnant, and Cassie appreciated Lisa's priorities lay with her much wanted baby.

Lisa had told Cassie that she would be returning to work part-time after having the baby and that her husband intended to reduce his hours too, in order to care for their new born. And why not? Cassie had thought, it made sense for each parent to spend quality time with their child.

'I think Lisa would make an excellent assistant manager,' Cassie said, looking for his reaction.

'Lisa?' he replied surprised.

'Yes. Would you consider making it a part-time role, or even a shared role?'

'Has Lisa ever expressed a wish to do managerial work? It would involve more training and would she want that, being a new mother?'

'Plenty of new mothers undergo training,' she reminded him.

'Yes, perhaps speak to her about it? Get her thoughts?'

'Will do,' she nodded.

Towards the end of her shift later in the day, Cassie approached Lisa. She was in the office sorting out the invoices. 'Lisa, can I have a word with you?' Lisa looked up, a little confused.

'Is there anything wrong?'

'No, not at all. In fact, come on, let's go for a coffee. I want to run something by you.'

Together they ordered coffees at the bar and sat in a quiet alcove. Cassie ran the whole scenario past Lisa and waited for her answer. A slow smile spread across Lisa's face.

'Oh Cassie, that's wonderful news,' she gasped.

'What about the timing?' asked Cassie. 'Might it be too much with a newborn?'

'I don't think so. After my maternity leave I was always coming back to work, part-time that is. So why not train and better myself?' Then she added, 'It will be more money, right?'

'Of course,' smiled Cassie, 'considerably more actually.' That earned her another big smile.

'Yes,' Lisa nodded her head decisively. 'I'd like to be considered, when the time comes.'

Chapter 29

Fletcher rubbed his hands. Tonight was the stag do and Jasper had given permission for him to enjoy a couple of whiskies at the inn. It wasn't just the drink he was looking forward to, it was the male bonhomie. He couldn't remember the last time he'd had such company, it had been so long. He opened his wardrobe and assessed what to wear. Fletcher had been a bit of a party animal in his day, forever entertaining; his midsummer balls had been notorious and he had always had a family party at Christmas. The Laurels had looked resplendent in those days, decorated to the brim, roaring log fires and carols merrily playing from the family's old gramophone. His wardrobe reflected how sociable he'd been back then, from pristine black dinner suits with silk lapels, starched collared white shirts, a variety of jackets with matching pocket squares, multicoloured blazers and mole-skin trousers, tweeds and waistcoats, brogues, boots, a vast selection of ties and hats, the list was endless. It was a collection accumulated and added to over a lifetime.

Fletcher was quite proud of his extensive wardrobe. He liked having an outfit for every occasion, and tonight he was determined to mark as an important one. It was Jasper's stag do and he, as best man, had to look the part.

He scraped the coat hangers across the pole, deciding which britches to wear. He'd go for the Donegal tweeds, yes that should strike the right note, along with the matching waistcoat and cream shirt.

'Ah, Fletcher there you are,' said Lilly from the doorway. 'Fancy a cup of tea?'

'Not at the moment lass, I'm just deciding my outfit for tonight.'

Lilly smiled to herself, finding his obvious excitement for the evening out endearing. She too, had had a wonderful night on Adira's hen do. Visions of them all swaying and singing along to the music in the restaurant gave her a much-needed boost after all this drama with Fletcher's health, particularly seeing Ruby enjoying herself so much. In fact, ever since the Scottish holiday, Ruby had seemed on much better form all together. She suspected Alfred had a lot to do with it. He'd clearly kept in touch. There had been a letter posted through the door the other day, in a thick cream envelope with neat black handwriting addressed to Ruby. Lilly had been sure it was from Alfred, judging by the Cheshire cat smile her sister had given her. Yes, something was certainly floating Ruby's boat. And long may it continue if this was the good mood it generated.

Lilly noticed the tweed trousers and waistcoat hanging on the side of the wardrobe.

'Very nice choice,' she said.

'Aye, it'll do.'

Lilly looked warily at him.

'Just behave yourself tonight,' she warned. 'Don't go overboard.'

Fletcher threw his head back and laughed.

'We've got to give the lad a good send off!'

Adira was in The Cobbled Courtyard. She had gone to collect the wedding favours made by Max and Fitz. She stepped inside Crafty Carpentry's studio and was greeted by the woody smell of pitch pine. Fitz had the doorstops ready in a crate by his workbench.

'Hi Adira, come in.' He took one out and passed it her.

'Oh, Fitz!' she exclaimed. The cute little campervan had been carved meticulously, totally capturing the Volkswagen shape and style. This was a nod to her own campervan she had nicknamed Sheila, as it was an Aussie import. It was thanks to Sheila that she had stumbled upon Lilacwell in the first place and so it only seemed right and proper to salute her. 'They're amazing.' She shook her head in wonder at all the detail, from the tiny windscreen wipers to the clever registration number plate, 'JH4AS' incorporating hers and Jasper's initials. 'Thanks a lot. How much do I owe you?'

'It's OK, they're on the house.'

'No, really Fitz—'

'Take them as my wedding gift,' he smiled interrupting her.

'Oh thanks, really. They're absolutely brilliant.'

'My pleasure,' he said, passing her the crate.

Adira put it in her car then made for The Hot Spot. Max was busy hammering iron, then sinking it into a vat of cold water. Steam filled the forge as she joined him.

'Hello there,' he grinned. 'Any pre-wedding nerves?'

'Not yet,' she laughed, 'but I'm sure there'll be a few on the big day.'

'You'll be fine,' he assured her. Then he went to collect the bottle openers he'd made. He passed a hessian sack over to her. She opened it and pulled one out to examine. They too had been beautifully crafted, with the black cast-iron handle twirling into a laurel-shaped leaf.

'Max, they're so elegant!' she gasped. He smiled, pleased with her reaction.

'Glad you like them.'

'I do.' She reached inside her bag for her purse, but Max stopped her.

'They're a gift,' he said, putting up his hands.

'Sure?'

'Absolutely.'

Touched once more by the Courtyard tenants' spirit of generosity, Adira clutched the sack close to her. 'Well, thanks Max, much appreciated.'

As she walked to her car, James waved a hello from his florist shop window. What a lovely bunch, she thought driving home. Lilacwell was looking so pretty with its bright Christmas lights swooping across the high street. All the window shops were beautifully displayed with decorations and the old-fashioned lampposts gently glowed in the early evening dusk. Never had she appreciated her surroundings more than in Lilacwell. For a second her mind cast back to last Christmas, when she'd been hustling amongst the busy, last-minute shoppers along Oxford Street. Whilst it, too, would have been brightly lit with lights, she'd have had little time to stop and admire them. She would have been in a hurry, anxious to buy the bare essentials then get back home to start working again. How time had passed her by, missing all the important things life had to offer. Well, not now. She lived in Lilacwell, not London. In precisely three days' time she was getting married to a wonderful, kind, gorgeous man and couldn't be happier. Just then her phone rang. Pulling into the side of the road, she saw that it was her gran and quickly answered.

'Hi, Gran.'

'Hello, darling. How are you?'

'I'm fine, thanks, and you?'

'No pre-wedding nerves?' Edie teased.

'Not yet. I'll probably have plenty on the day, though,' laughed Adira.

'I'm sure you've got it all under control,' assured Edie, then continued, 'Adira, I'm right in saying we're all staying on the campsite, aren't I?'

'Yes, Gran, your very own shepherds hut. Is that all right? You're welcome to stay in The Laurels, we've a spare guest room?' Adira had naturally assumed her gran and parents would appreciate their own space, rather than stay in the house with them.

'No, that's fine darling, really, I'm quite looking forward to a night under the stars,' Edie said smiling.

'What, you, Mum and Dad, all by the campfire?' joked Adira, laughing at the thought of her mother doing anything remotely like that. Whereas her gran she could easily imagine getting into the spirit of the great outdoors. 'Do you think Mum will be OK on the glamping site?'

Edie's mouth twitched at the term 'glamping' – it was still plain old camping when all said and done. When had it suddenly become glamorous? You were still pitching up a tent or sleeping in a caravan in a field. Honestly, the youth of today. But as for her daughter enjoying the experience? Hmm, she wasn't too sure about that. Cleo was renowned for her picky ways, never one to muck in with the rest of them. Secretly, she was half expecting her to check into a nearby hotel, but didn't want to admit that to Adira, for fear of disappointing her.

'She ought to be,' replied Edie diplomatically. 'Those shepherds huts look amazing.'

'Well, failing that, she can camp out in Sheila,' said Adira, the precious campervan being her pride and joy.

'High honour indeed! Right darling, I'll let you go. I'm sure you've a thousand and one things to do. See you in three days' time my love.'

'Bye, Gran.'

Suddenly, it all hit home. Adira sat in contemplation before starting up the car again. In just three days she would become a married woman. She would be Adira Hendricks, wife of Jasper Hendricks. Her life would change forever. Goosebumps covered her as an unstoppable grin spread across her face.

Chapter 30

Rory was late. He wasn't having a good day at all; everything was running against him. It had all started with the man driving the hire van turning up an hour late. Then it had taken longer than he'd expected to fill the van with all the boxes he'd packed. A last-minute phone call from his solicitor held him up even more, then, once on the road, traffic had piled up. When finally reaching the motorway, a huge sign warned of more delays and the closure of one lane. It was now early evening and he was getting anxious. The last thing he wanted was to miss Jasper's stag do. He was also eager to talk to Cassie but realised he wouldn't have time for that tonight.

He urgently tapped his steering wheel and glanced at the dashboard clock. It was six p.m. They were supposed to be meeting at the Inn for seven thirty. He'd be leaving the motorway at the next junction. Looking in his rear mirror, he was relieved to see the hire van still behind him. Together they were driving to Cassie's parents, then he had to unload all the boxes into the barn being used for storage. Time was against him.

At last they had vacated the motorway and were heading along the country roads leading to the Wrights' farm. Rory had phoned Cassie to tell her he'd be late. Fortunately, she and her parents were ready and waiting for him when he arrived, and immediately calm swept over him when seeing them all there, ready to help unload.

'Traffic's been a nightmare,' he said, getting out of his car.

Cassie gave him a hug. 'Never mind, you're safely here now.'

He quickly kissed her before turning to her parents. 'Thanks again for letting me use your barn.'

'No problem. Come on, let's get unpacked,' Cassie's dad replied.

'You'll have to go soon,' warned Cassie, looking at her watch. 'You've only got an hour until the stag do.'

'I know, let's move.'

After half an hour, with everyone's help, all the boxes had been shifted into the barn. The van driver had gone and Rory had to make his way back to the Inn. He badly needed a shower.

'You two go quick,' said Cassie's mum. 'We'll lock up here, go on.' She hurried them away.

Arriving at the Inn, Rory pelted up the stairs straight to Cassie's room and dived into the shower. Within fifteen minutes flat he was washed, dressed and raring to go. Cassie marvelled at how good he looked, with such little time to get ready. He wore dark jeans with a smart pale grey shirt, slightly opened to reveal a glimpse of dark hair. A spicy citrus fragrance wafted from him and his curls had been towel-dried, still slightly damp but enviably falling into place without need of styling. He quickly looked at his watch.

'Only five minutes late.'

'Don't worry, they won't all be here yet,' assured Cassie. It was her night off, which she was pleased about. The last thing she wanted to do was cramp the stag do, wandering around the hotel on shift. Instead, she had a relaxing night ahead of her which consisted of a long hot bubble bath, a glass of wine and a good book. Rory came over to give her a kiss.

'Tomorrow, we'll talk,' he said before placing his lips on hers. After a sensuous kiss, Cassie frowned at what he had just said.

'Talk about what?' she asked.

He raised an eyebrow.

'You tell me,' he replied.

'Rory?'

'Gotta go, see ya, Pixie.' And with that he quickly left, leaving Cassie in deep thought.

Downstairs in the bar, Fletcher's voice could be heard booming across the room. Already he was in fine form. On seeing Rory enter he called out.

'What are you drinking, Rory?'

Rory looked a tad surprised at how familiar Fletcher seemed, given as he had only met him a couple of times. Jasper gave him a knowing look and laughed, confident that by the end of the night, Fletcher would be everybody's best mate.

'Err… I'll have a pint of Hen Harrier, thanks,' replied Rory.

'Good choice!' bellowed back Fletcher.

Jasper made his way over to Rory. 'Thanks for coming.'

'Thanks for the invite, sorry I'm late. I've only just got back from London.'

'Finally made the move then?' Jasper smiled.

'Yeah,' replied Rory, 'and it feels good. Very good. Now I just need to find the perfect place to live.'

Jasper nodded. He knew from Adira that Rory was looking locally and it made him think.

'There you go,' Fletcher butted in and passed Rory his drink.

'Thanks, Fletcher.' Rory took a long drink. Hell, he needed that after the day he'd had.

'Come on, I'll introduce you to everyone.' Jasper ushered him towards a large table in the corner which had been designated 'the stag table'. Max and Fitz had been the first to arrive, followed by Colin, who Jasper had wanted to include. James was just returning from the bar with a nice claret and old Dickie was sat comfortably in the fireside chair they had moved to the stag table. Jasper introduced Rory to them all.

James was particularly chatty with him, interested in where he had lived in London and his job as a barrister.

'So, can I ask,' James spoke animatedly, moving his free hand, whilst holding his wine glass by the stem with the other, 'how do you defend someone who you really believe to be guilty?'

Rory smiled at the question, which was a common one asked of many barristers.

'I try not to pre-judge,' he answered politely. Then his attention turned to Max. So, this was the black-smith. Here, he *had* pre-judged and with good reason he'd thought. He noticed the way Max's eyes followed the women in the pub, eyeing them up. One or two stopped to make conversation with him. Rory took in the easy, self-confident way he had with them, obviously charming, if the ladies' giggles and grins had anything to go by. Smooth bastard. He also noticed Jasper attract quite a bit of attention, albeit on a friendly rather than flirty level. Fitz seemed a nice enough chap, although quiet, the complete opposite to Fletcher, who could still be heard barking out the drinks orders.

'Another whisky please, lass,' he called to Lisa who was working behind the bar, 'and a pint for all the stags!' he added.

'Just how many whiskies have you had, Fletcher?' asked Jasper with narrowed eyes.

'Oh… only one or two,' Fletcher's voice quietened. 'Now come on, lad, cut me some slack, it is your stag do.'

'Hmm, go easy,' Jasper replied with concern. 'Promise?'

'Aye, don't worry,' Fletcher nodded sagely.

Rory was touched by the exchange. The affection between the two of them was obvious.

'Excuse me?' One of the ladies who'd been talking to Max had sidled up behind Rory. He turned to face a small blonde with big blue eyes, wearing skinny jeans, riding boots and a fitted tweed jacket. Very country set, probably owns a horse called Truffles, thought Rory amusingly. 'Aren't you the guy who defended the activists? The Climate… err…'

'Warrior,' said Max on his way to the bar, overhearing the conversation.

Rory's eyes slid over him. Was that a smirk?

'Oh yes!' chirped the girl. 'The Climate Warrior!'

A few of the people surrounding them stopped as her voice carried across the room and stared at Rory momentarily before carrying on chatting. Rory felt put on the spot. Max was at the bar now, chatting to Lisa.

'Yes, I defended the activists,' replied Rory in a cool voice, suddenly disliking this woman who was embarrassing him and intruding on his time with his stag do companions.

'Oh, how marvellous!' she gushed. 'I so admire your ethics. Tell me, how do you represent people who you suspect are—'

'I represented the demonstrators wholeheartedly. I am one,' Rory cut in bluntly.

'Oh.' She fluttered her eyelashes, clearly impressed, achieving the opposite effect Rory had intended. Then, to his horror, she waved her friends over.

'Excuse me,' he swiftly made an exit to the bar. Fortunately, Max had been served so he wouldn't have to talk to him either. Lisa gave him a cheery smile and served him.

'I'll get this,' Jasper said, suddenly appearing.

'Thanks,' Rory nodded.

'Actually, could I have a word, Rory?'

Rory looked quizzically at him, wondering what it was Jasper could have to say to him. 'It won't take long.' Jasper ushered him outside the bar, into the hotel entrance area, where it was quieter. 'There's something I think you may be interested in.'

Jasper told Rory about the barn that he was in the process of obtaining planning permission for, so he could renovate it along with the land surrounding it. Rory listened intently, giving his full attention. It sounded ideal, it really did. But how much would Jasper be asking for it? Ever since looking at the old farmhouse in Chipping, Rory had become a little wary about property needing a lot of work. 'Come and have a look tomorrow,' said Jasper. 'See what you think.'

'I will,' replied Rory, reluctant to ask the price at this stage. 'Now come on, you've a stag do to enjoy,' he grinned. Adira was right, Jasper really was an astute businessman to be drumming up deals on tonight of all nights.

'More drinks over here!' Fletcher's voice could be heard reverberating round the bar, again.

After much drinking, cheering and male camaraderie, all finished off with the inevitable 'down-in-ones', the stags had to finally say do at last orders.

'Lock in!' shouted Fletcher who was immediately silenced by Jasper.

'Fletcher, enough. We're going home,' he told him, as sternly as he could slur.

'Aye, all right lad, let's be off,' said Fletcher, knowing when he was beaten.

Taxis had all been booked to arrive at the same time to take them home. Adira had seen to that, not relishing the idea of picking up two drunken Hendricks. And drunk they were, as they fell out of the taxi and staggered up The Laurels' doorsteps. Jasper had difficulty finding his key, then struggled even more trying to put it into the lock.

'Hurry up, Jasper!' hissed Fletcher, 'I'm bursting.'

'Shush, you'll wake Adira,' Jasper mumbled, then grunted with satisfaction at getting the key to turn and open the door.

Fletcher dashed, as quickly as an inebriated eighty-five-year-old could, to the cloakroom. Jasper rolled his eyes at hearing the loud sigh of relief come from the door. He sat, waiting on the bottom stair to take him upstairs to bed. There was no way he could leave Fletcher to take care of himself. At last Fletcher swaggered into the hall, marginally missing the console table and gripped the banister post.

'Well, what a cracking night that was,' he said, then hiccupped.

Jasper couldn't help but chuckle. The old boy had out-drunk them all. So much for the two whiskies only rule. More like two bottles.

'Come on, you. Bed.' Together they stumbled, arm in arm up the stairs, tittering all the way.

Meanwhile, Adira, who'd been lying awake, waiting for their return, smiled to herself and turned over to snuggle into a peaceful sleep.

Cassie hadn't slept a wink. She too had been waiting for Rory to return. What had he meant about 'talking tomorrow' and 'you tell me'? Her mind was spinning with questions. At last she heard his footsteps on the corridor and the door open. He tripped and cursed, then made his way to the bathroom. After what seemed an age, he tried his best to creep into bed, but stubbed his toe and cursed again, then flopped with a thud next to her.

'Rory?' she whispered, but all she got was a faint groan. 'Rory,' she tried again, louder this time. Still no answer, just the sound of soft snoring coming from him. Sighing with impatience, Cassie turned her back on him.

Chapter 31

It was late morning by the time Rory finally surfaced, much to the annoyance of Cassie, who was still burning with curiosity over their 'talk'. Predicting he would have the mother of all hangovers, she placed a packet of paracetamols and a glass of water on the bedside table for him.

Gradually waking, he yawned, rubbed his eyes and slowly sat up. Cassie had showered, dressed and was on her laptop.

'Ah, still living then?' she teased.

'Just about,' he mumbled then reached for his water and tablets. 'Thanks for these,' he said after downing the full glass. He looked at Cassie, concentrating on her screen. 'What are you looking at?'

'What do you think? Property,' she replied, not taking her eyes off the laptop.

'We might have found the right one,' he replied.

This got her attention. Suddenly she was all ears.

'What do you mean?' she asked sharply, eager to know.

Rory outlined all the details of the barn on the Hendricks' estate and how Jasper had invited them to look at it that day. Cassie sat transfixed, taking everything in.

'But that sounds ideal!' she squealed with delight.

'That's what I thought,' replied Rory, 'but we must be cautious. We don't know how much Jasper will want for it. It sounds like it needs a lot of work doing to it.'

'Yes,' agreed Cassie, ever mindful of the dilapidated farmhouse they'd viewed. 'We'll have a better idea once we've seen it, though, and at least we know Jasper won't want to rip us off.'

'There is that,' nodded Rory, 'but he is a businessman at the end of the day, Cass,' he tried to warn her.

'A fair one,' she replied instantly, 'just like Fletcher was. My dad can vouch for that.'

'Let's not get too excited.' Rory hated the idea of having their hopes dashed again.

'Come on, get up. I'll order us some breakfast, then we can go.'

Rory smiled to himself. Whilst he was trying to keep a level head, it has hard not to enjoy seeing Cassie so energised. Living on The Laurels estate, right next door to her best mate, in the beloved village she'd grown up in and loved, was the perfect move for her. How could she possibly keep calm? He too, was warming to the idea of having friends for neighbours. He was keen to see the land, too, hoping it was suitable for a smallholding.

—

Jasper was in the estate office with Colin. They had all the paperwork concerning the planning application for the barn. As an attractive, traditional, stone-built barn, the council had given permission for change of use to the building. Detailed planning approval would be needed before any work started and Jasper was intending to sell the property with the new owner taking the barn on as a self-build project. All this would be reflected in the price of course. Rory struck him as a man who would want to be in total control of the build, so didn't envisage this being a problem – *if* Rory wanted to buy it. In many ways Jasper considered the arrangement would suit them both; he wanted rid of the barn and field with the least hassle at an honest price, while Rory, he suspected, wanted to create an eco home, as economically as possible with his own design and ideas. The field was more than adequate to accommodate a smallholding. Plus, the river running through the edge of it gave further possibilities for an eco-friendly lifestyle.

'A professional ecological assessment will be required,' Colin told Jasper, 'to determine if the work on the barn will have any impact on trees, owls, bats or newts.' He was reading through the council's notes.

'We'll let Rory study the paperwork. As a barrister, I'm sure he'll want to read all the small print,' answered Jasper with confidence.

It wasn't long before they heard a tap on the door. Jasper got up and welcomed the two in. Immediately he caught Cassie's upbeat vibe, while Rory looked calm and reserved.

'Adira's busy at the moment,' he explained, to which Cassie burst out laughing.

'Well yeah, considering you're getting married tomorrow, I guess she is.'

Jasper smiled wryly. Rory on the other hand took heed of this. It further confirmed his earlier opinion of him – that he was an astute businessman, to be this preoccupied with his estate on the eve of his wedding. Above all, Rory was desperate to keep a clear mind in any possible transaction. Not wanting his heart to rule his head, like it had so many times in the past. For once he was determined to exercise prudence and not delve in feet first, as he was notorious for.

'So, here is all the paperwork, Rory, concerning the council's approval for renovation. Please, take a seat.'

Cassie and Rory sat next to Colin, who explained each document. Most of it went over Cassie's head; she was too impatient to look at the barn itself and see where it was. Rory however studied them, his eyes scanning each page, taking in all the information. After several minutes, he raised his head.

'Can I have copies of these?'

'Of course,' replied Jasper.

'I can deal with that.' Colin rose and took the documents to photocopy them.

'Come on, I'll show you the barn,' said Jasper as Colin was busy.

At last, thought Cassie, practically leaping from her chair.

Jasper led them to the far west field. All the time Rory's eyes were sweeping over the land. Yes, it was good for crop growing, judging by the adjacent fields which had been ploughed and obviously harvested. Entering the field, Jasper explained that it had previously belonged to a farm of one of his tenants, reaffirming to Rory that it must have been put to agricultural use before, all good signs. Then they came to the barn. The new gable end was built to a high standard, giving them some indication as to how the whole of the building could look. The roof needed ripping off altogether. As Rory wanted roof-mounted solar panelling, he anticipated he would need to build a stronger structure to hold them anyway. So replacing the roof was already in his budget.

'I can give you the name of the builders who fixed the gable end,' Jasper told them, seeing that Rory was impressed with their work.

'Good,' nodded Rory. Then he assessed the huge barn door, rotten and dismantled from the iron track. He would like to replace this with an exact replica, eager to preserve the barn's original form. The track he could easily restore. Wherever possible, he wanted to reuse materials or use like-for-like, keen to apply a light touch and keep the original character.

Cassie too, was envisaging the restoration, imagining large picture windows overlooking the stunning views surrounding them. Already in her mind it was a done deal. She glanced sideways for Rory's reaction. He didn't seem to be giving anything away, though, not like their previous viewing of the farmhouse. Please let this be the one, she prayed inside. It was too good to pass up. The barn could look magnificent if given the right amount of love and attention (and money), which they surely could, couldn't they? Again she looked at Rory, but still he looked poker faced.

'The river runs through the edge of the field,' Jasper said, pointing to the far end.

'Have you fishing rights?' asked Rory, remembering what the estate agent had told them from the Chipping farm property.

'Yes,' replied Jasper, then added, 'You could build your own waterwheel if you wanted.'

Rory's eyes widened, unable to hide this pleasant surprise, making Cassie smother a chuckle. This proved to be the clincher.

'Let's talk money then, Jasper. What do you want for it?' asked Rory directly. His heart was pounding in his chest. He wanted it. He could tell Cassie wanted it, and he was pretty sure Jasper knew this. It was all hinging on his reply.

'Given the amount of land and the state of the barn, I'm asking £350,000.'

Cassie's head turned sharply to Rory.

'Let me look over the paperwork again and I'll give you an answer tomorrow,' replied Rory as coolly as he could. The price he suspected was a fair one, but still he had to consider his budget and the amount of work needing paying for.

'Jasper is getting married tomorrow!' exclaimed Cassie in frustration. Left to her, she'd have signed on the dotted line within the hour.

'Rory's right. Take your time. I don't want to hurry you,' said Jasper reassuringly, then added half laughing, 'and yes, I'll be pretty busy tomorrow, the end of the week will do.'

'When do you fly to Dubai?' asked Cassie.

'Not till the third of January, so there's no rush.'

'Has Adira guessed where you're going yet?' Cassie smiled.

'Not a clue. I hope she'll like it.'

'I'm sure she'll appreciate the sunshine and the warmth,' remarked Rory looking round the beautiful, but bitterly cold, frosted fields and glistening fir trees in the distance.

'I wouldn't swap this for the desert,' replied Cassie. 'You can't beat Christmas in Lilacwell.'

—

After such an eventful day, Cassie had forgotten to ask Rory about 'the talk' he had wanted. Rory too, was deep in thought about the barn. Finance-wise he thought they would manage it. He already had the bulk of the price of the barn, but he would need a loan to renovate it. Having done his research, he planned to approach the Ecology Building Society, who lent on out-of-the-ordinary projects which significantly improved a building's eco credentials. Which was exactly what Rory intended to do; he wanted to produce as much energy as he could, as efficiently as possible by installing solar thermal power. Long term he thought they could accomplish all that they wanted.

Cassie hadn't stopped talking about it. She was reaching fever pitch. Whereas she was visualising the decor and deciding on kitchens and bathrooms, Rory was concentrating on solar collectors and batteries. It was only in the evening, whilst they were sat having dinner in the bar, did she remember to broach the subject which had been niggling away at her. Then, on impulse, she took the bull by the horns. Why not?

'Rory?'

'Hmm?' he reached for his pint glass.

'Will you marry me?'

He stopped mid-drink and blinked. Then, putting his glass down, looked deep into her eyes.

'In a heartbeat, Pixie.' They sat staring at each other.

'When?' pressed Cassie with a smile on her face.

'Well, we're gonna be busy,' he laughed, 'and skint.'

'Adira once commented that she thought you'd want to elope.'

'Sounds good to me,' he replied with a shrug.

'Really?'

'Yeah, let's do it.' Then, the penny dropped. 'So that's what was on your mind the other day?' he asked grinning. 'I thought there was something bothering you.'

She smiled, not answering. Rory took her hand in his. 'You know I love you, more than anything?'

'And I you,' she gulped, on the verge of tears. She could not recall being so blissfully happy in her entire life.

Chapter 32

Today was the day. The Laurels was looking splendid, fit for the Christmas wedding it was about to host. The hall was decked with holly, berries and mistletoe entwined through the staircase spindles, all the way across the balcony, along with hanging lanterns. The Christmas tree was glimmering in all its glory, shining with fairy lights, baubles and various trinkets: some old, belonging to the family for years; some new, which Adira had bought for the occasion. The air was filled with the scent of the seasonal foliage decorations – pine cones and rustic logs covered in ivy, deep red roses, winter white lilies and cinnamon-scented candles.

The kitchen was busy with the catering team preparing mini mince pies and mulled wine, instead of the usual canapés and bubbly. Adira had opted for a real Christmas feel, having also chosen to go with traditional turkey for the main meal and Christmas pudding for dessert.

Festive hymns and carols were playing in the background and open fires crackled with warmth. It all reminded Fletcher of Christmases past at The Laurels and a profound contentment filled his soul. There was only *one* thing which could potentially colour this day. Alice and Rufus would be here. His brother and sister-in-law naturally would be at Jasper's wedding, but it didn't make matters easy for him. Still, today wasn't about *him*. It was all about Jasper. Jasper and Adira, it was their special day and nothing was going to ruin it. The Laurels was a big enough place to avoid them, Fletcher told himself as he fastened his tie. He then stepped back to admire himself in the full-length mirror. Not bad, not bad at all, he thought, inspecting the dark grey morning suit. The splash of deep red in the tie and pocket square really gave the outfit that touch of style he was renowned for.

Jasper was doing the very same thing in his own room, but his mind was on Adira, not his own appearance. He worried that she wouldn't be happy with his choice of honeymoon. She had spent so much time and energy on the wedding preparations, he only hoped Dubai would come up trumps. She, more than anyone, deserved a well-earned holiday.

Adira was way too preoccupied to think about anything beyond the wedding ceremony. She'd been up since seven a.m. sorting the flower delivery from James's florist, overseeing the caterers and making sure all the wine and champagne had been brought up from the cellar. Her parents and gran had arrived yesterday and to her relief were quite taken with their little shepherds huts. She had made sure the woodburners had been lit in advance, making the huts nice and cosy for their arrival.

Once happy with all the arrangements downstairs, she sank into a heavenly bubble bath, then her gran was going to help her get ready. Nobody could do her hair as well as Gran. Ever since she was a little girl, Edie had brushed her golden locks till they shone, then put the strands up in elegant chignon buns, French pleats or tight, neat braids. Her mother had never had the inclination or time to spend on her hair. Today, Adira wanted to wear it down, in thick ringlets cascading down her back, the way Jasper liked it. Simple, but effective and Gran would get it just right, like she always did. Adira looked at the vintage wedding dress hanging patiently on the wardrobe. How graceful it looked with its ivory lace and beading. A frisson of excitement shot through her. She was actually getting married!

—

Cassie and Rory were on cloud nine. Even they, the spur-of-the-moment couple, conceded how fast their lives were about to take a dramatic change. Together, after rereading all the documentation of the barn, they had made a decision. They were going for it, big time. They were going to buy and restore the barn into an eco-friendly home and create a smallholding to become as self-sufficient as possible. Oh yes, and they were also eloping.

Rory had at least told his parents of his plans and promised to visit them with Cassie very soon. He was slightly concerned about their reaction, yet needn't have been. Nobody more than they were used to their wayward, impetuous son. 'Typical runaway train, Rory,' sighed his mother, knowing full well that to object in any way was futile. Rory knew his own mind; he always had. Plus, his parents had never heard him so happy.

Now getting ready for the wedding, Rory reflected that he didn't miss wearing a collar and tie every day as he adjusted his navy suit. Cassie wore a slim fitted plum woollen dress and brown suede boots. A lilac pashmina finished the outfit off nicely. Rory gave her a wolf whistle.

'You don't look so bad yourself,' laughed Cassie. Suddenly Rory's face clouded over. 'What?' she asked concerned.

'I was just thinking, you won't regret us not having a family wedding like Adira and Jasper?'

'No,' Cassie replied with certainty. 'I rather like the idea of running off in secret, it's so romantic.'

'Yes, it is,' agreed Rory, then stopped himself from adding, 'and cheap'.

–

All the guests made their way up the footpath in the late afternoon dusk to The Laurels. The orangery was illumin-ated with pillar candles and hurricane lamps, giving a soft, mellow glow. White roses and winter greenery decorated the sills and the table at the front, covered with white linen, held a large bouquet of red poinsettias.

In they came, shuffling sideways into their chairs. Max and Fitz sat at the back, along with Colin. James, however, wanted a ringside view and placed himself on the second row. Acting as witnesses, Cassie and Rory were at the front, alongside Adira's mother and gran. Fletcher stood proudly with Jasper at the front, in the centre aisle, before the registrar. Alice and Rufus sat alone at the far end of the top row. The rest of the guests filled the seats and waited for the bride to make an entrance.

An excited anticipation filled the air and then suddenly the sound of 'Silent Night' echoed through the orangery. The room's eyes turned to Adira as she walked serenely on her father's arm down the middle to join Jasper. As she did, he turned to face her and the burning desire oozing from him was palpable.

Together, with their loved ones watching, Adira and Jasper made their vows to each other. Edie's eyes filled with emotion when the registrar announced them husband and wife. A cheer exploded from the small gathering, making the happy couple laugh into each other. As they turned to walk back through them, hand in hand, rose petals were thrown as confetti (a touch suggested by James). 'Deck the Halls' rang out as they made their way into the hall, where staff carrying silver trays of mulled wine greeted them.

'I love you, Mrs Hendricks,' Jasper gazed at Adira and kissed her on the lips. Fletcher who was stood nearby and overheard, stilled for a moment, his heart melting at Jasper's words. Then his eye caught Alice's across the hall. There she was, looking as radiant as ever. She was as beautiful now as the day he first met her. His mind cast back to all those years ago, when his little brother had proudly introduced his family to his new girlfriend. How taken they all were with this young beauty on Rufus's arm, full of life and exuberance. Sadly, that had been sapped of her over the time. It had been evidently clear to Fletcher how miserable Rufus had made Alice, much to his frustration. For he, more than anyone, knew how badly matched they were. Fletcher had longed to love and look after Alice, if only she had let him because he was certain she felt the same. The chemistry between them couldn't be denied. Only once had she allowed them to share their true feelings, and Jasper was the result of that one, precious union. Fletcher looked deeply into those mesmerising pale eyes. *Why, Alice?* I could have made you so happy.

'Drink, Fletcher?' Lilly interrupted his thoughts. He turned and smiled, taking a glass off her. Lilly had been his rock, a true friend and companion. Her loyalty deserved his full attention.

'May I say how pretty you look today?' Then he bent down to whisper, 'And Ruby's scrubbed up well too,' he added, his eyes twinkling with mischief. This earned him a playful nudge from Lilly.

After a short while all the photographs had been taken, and the guests were shown into the huge dining room. The long table running down the centre shone with silverware, crystal and candelabras. The wedding favours made by Fitz and Max went down a treat. Here they enjoyed a time-honoured Christmas dinner.

When Adira's father rose to give his speech, silence hung in the air. As predicted, he made it short and sweet, not one for public speaking. Fletcher, on the other hand, milked the opportunity to be given a platform. He spoke with true love and affection of Jasper's childhood days at The Laurels, making Adira's eyes fill. It was blatantly obvious to all how much Jasper meant to him, and how pleased he was with his choice of bride. His comment on them having 'a white witch' in the family made all the guests roar with laughter. But it was his last comment which resonated with everyone present. 'Jasper is and will always be my world.' There wasn't a dry eye in the house. Apart from Rufus.

'Well, how do I follow that?' said Jasper when it was his turn to speak. He then continued, giving his thanks to all for attending. He turned to Fletcher and gave his sincere gratitude for all he was – simply the best role model ever. Then he faced Adira and told them all what an honour it was to have such a stunning bride and soulmate for life. A tear trickled down her face, which she hastily wiped away. Finally, Jasper raised his champagne flute and gave a toast. 'To my wonderful wife!' he cheered.

As darkness descended, everyone made their way onto the lawn for the firework display. Bright colours popped, banged and sparkled into the night sky. Hot toddies were passed round and blankets for those needing them.

'It's been amazing,' said Adira as Jasper put his arm round her.

'And it's not over yet,' he kissed her cheek.

'So, are you now going to tell me where we are going on honeymoon?' she asked smiling. Jasper looked into her blue eyes, the lights from the fireworks reflecting in them.

'Dubai,' he replied, closely observing her reaction.

'Dubai? Of course, why hadn't I guessed?' she beamed, much to his relief. Then they both looked up, hearing a collective. 'Aw!' from the gathering. There, in the pitch blackness of the sky, fireworks lit up a huge 'J' and 'A' surrounded by a heart shape. It really had been the most magical of days.

Chapter 33

There was a hive of activity the next morning at The Laurels. Adira's parents and gran were coming for breakfast and the plan was for them to stay over for Christmas before returning home. Lilly was in the kitchen with Fletcher fussing over the preparations.

'Do you think we should sit in the dining room?' she asked anxiously.

'Oh, stop flapping, Lilly. We'll be grand in here.'

The kitchen was indeed perfectly fine to host a family breakfast, with its granite-topped island with high stools and long farmhouse table, surrounded by leather padded chairs. It was a far cry from the old one, with its creaky, wooden units and Formica surfaces. The kitchen had been one of the first rooms Jasper had renovated. He'd thoroughly enjoyed ripping out the old, damp cupboards and replacing them with fresh, modern ones, along with integrated appliances and vibrant coloured splash backs. Now, instead of a tired looking sixties affair, with orange and brown swirled tiles, metal sink and pantry, a solid oak kitchen shone with black granite tops. There was a butler sink with copper taps and it had a separate utility room to put the noisy washing machine in. The new Aga oven made sure the place was permanently cosy and warm too.

Lilly had never known such fanciness, when first seeing the finished kitchen, to the point where she felt a touch uncomfortable using it, not wanting to stain or damage any of the pristine appliances. But now, after a few months, she'd grown accustomed to it. The new dishwasher was a godsend and she'd often wondered how she'd coped before ever having had it. The large silver top-of-the-range coffee maker however she had mastered long since. Even Fletcher knew how to handle this, as it was the first thing Jasper had bought on his return to The Laurels. It had been a no-brainer for him, insisting that they had to have a decent coffee.

'What time are they coming?' asked Fletcher, perching on the edge of a stool at the island.

'Any minute now.' Lilly frowned. 'Where's Jasper and Adira?' she asked, looking at the kitchen clock. Fletcher gave a low rumble of laughter.

'I should imagine they've been busy, Lilly,' he smirked, 'with it being their wedding night and all.' Lilly blushed slightly and carried on busying herself. Fletcher smiled to himself, finding her embarrassment rather endearing. Just then, in they came, the newlyweds themselves. 'Ah, here they are!' cheered Fletcher, then tapped a stool next to him. 'Come and sit down, Mrs Hendricks,' he winked at Adira. She smiled and took a croissant from the plate on the Aga.

'This smells good Lilly,' Jasper said, helping himself to the coffee machine.

'Oh, I hope everything's all right for them,' she replied, flustering with the bacon on the grill pan.

'Lilly, I said *stop flapping*,' warned Fletcher.

'Sit down, Lilly. We'll sort this out,' Adira said, joining Jasper. 'Really,' she ushered Lilly to sit down, 'it's fine.' Then they heard the doorbell ring and Lilly shot off to answer it.

Soon they were all sat round the big kitchen table sipping coffee and tea, passing round the croissants. Then Jasper and Adira dished out the full English breakfast that had been warming in the Aga.

'Hmm, this looks delicious,' said Edie, mouth practically watering.

'It certainly does,' replied Fletcher. Then he patted Lilly's lap. 'Thanks, lass.'

'Yes, thank you, Lilly,' smiled Cleo. She turned to face Fletcher, 'And thank you so much for your wonderful hospitality.'

'Here, here,' agreed Pat. He was delighted that his daughter had married into such a warm, loving family. He was also equally delighted to see his wife relax and unwind for once. A deep, comforting feeling told him that the Hendricks family and The Laurels were going to have a huge impact on their lives – and all for the better.

'This really is the most charming of places,' remarked Edie, gazing out of the new French doors, leading onto a kitchen garden. It consisted of raised vegetable beds, pots of herbs and a quaint Victorian greenhouse. Adira grinned, knowing full well how her gran appreciated The Laurels. She was glad it had made such a good impression on her parents as well. After all, this was her home now and they would be spending a lot of time here too.

'It is,' agreed Jasper. 'I've had a wonderful childhood in this place.'

Cleo's forehead creased in confusion, then she asked, 'Where do your parents live, Jasper?'

It was an innocent enough question, prompted by the mention of Jasper's childhood, but with an underlying implication, querying why his childhood was spent at The Laurels with Fletcher, rather than with his parents.

Jasper easily batted away any uncomfortable tension. He'd noticed Fletcher's jaw tighten.

'In Cumbria, but I spent most of my school holidays here,' he casually replied with a smile. 'It was tremendous fun to be on The Laurels estate with Fletcher.' Then added, looking at him, 'Wasn't it?'

'Oh, it was,' chuckled Fletcher. 'The tales I could tell you.' His eyes scanned round the table mischievously, making them all laugh.

There was no doubt about it, thought Adira, Fletcher had charisma. He could charm the birds from the trees. She sat and listened to him, in full flow, regaling family stories from the past, all interwoven with humour. Like when he was naughty, little Jasper had hidden a mouse in the old butler's bed.

'Poor old Wilson, no wonder he buggered off with the housekeeper!' roared Fletcher, throwing his head back. He had everyone in raptures, even Cleo, who was wiping her eyes from laughter. Adira found it fascinating, hearing about Jasper as a child. Then Edie caught her eye and gave her a huge warm smile. Adira returned it, as a mutual understanding. She knew right enough, '*You've chosen well, my darling*,' was the message. Her phone bleeped with a text message.

> Rory told me not to contact you today, but I can't help it! We want the barn!

Adira rolled her eyes and laughed gently. Typical Cassie.

'What?' smiled Jasper, seeing her amused.

'Just read this,' she replied passing her phone. Jasper gave a wry grin.

'Typical Cassie,' he said.

'That's exactly what I thought,' Adira replied.

'I'll tell Colin to get in contact with them.' Then added laughing, 'Or she'll no doubt be following us all the way to Dubai.'

After a hearty start to the day, Adira's parents and gran said they intended to go on a long walk and explore the area. Fletcher and Lilly offered to go with them and show them the many points of interest.

'We'll give the newlyweds some quality time together,' he winked, making Jasper shake his head. Adira giggled; she was more than used to Fletcher's sense of humour now. Cleo chose to ignore the comment.

'We could stop for lunch at the Inn at Lilacwell?' she suggested.

'Oh, that would be lovely,' chirped Lilly.

'Our treat,' said Pat, then seeing Fletcher about to object continued, 'No I insist, it's the least we can do.'

Off they went, chatting all the way down the gravel driveway.

Jasper and Adira turned and smiled at each other.

'That went well,' said Jasper, putting an arm round her waist, pulling her into him.

'Yes, they do seem to get along. I don't think I've seen my mum so chilled,' she replied. She looked out of the hall window into the distance at the snow-capped hills and frosted greenery. Lilacwell had been the perfect place for a Christmas wedding and it had certainly worked its magic on her family.

'I'll just make a quick call to Colin. Put Cassie out of her misery.' Jasper reached for his mobile.

'She'll be on pins,' laughed Adira.

'To be fair, I did tell Rory to contact me before we went away.'

'Ah yes, Dubai,' she beamed. 'Bring on the sunshine.'

'Well, it'll be a damn sight warmer than here,' he grinned.

'Yes, but it won't be home.' Adira once again took in the stunning winter scenery outside. Jasper was touched to hear his new wife call Lilacwell 'home'.

Chapter 34

Cassie was beside herself with joy. As per Jasper's instructions, Colin had indeed contacted Rory. Together they had arranged a meeting to begin the procedure of the sale of the barn.

No matter how many times Rory had cautioned Cassie to 'calm down', she was simply unable to do so. That said, he too couldn't wipe the wide smile off his face. And why should he? His ultimate ambition of living an eco, self-sufficient lifestyle looked like it was *actually* going to happen. Rory could hardly believe it. All those years of working at Goldgate Chambers, day in, day out, had finally paid off. Big time. His commitment and dedication to his career as a barrister, which he'd studied so hard for, had enabled him to save a substantial amount of money. All those nights spent cooped up in his apartment, instead of painting the town red, had saved him even more. Living virtually like a hermit had proved fruitful. That and the profit made from selling his flat had given him a healthy budget. Cassie's contribution wasn't on the same scale, being considerably smaller, but was valued all the same. Rory was at pains not to make her feel in anyway inadequate. They were a team, on a joint venture and he intended to open joint accounts. From now on they were in it together. Even he, whirlwind that he was, conceded how quickly the events of his life were unravelling. Yet despite this, he knew it was all *right*. Never, at any stage, had he ever doubted his actions. If anyone had told him a year ago just how things were going to pan out, he wouldn't have believed them. Although it would certainly have cheered him up, especially on those lonely nights when his head had been buried in law books.

In his quieter moments, all sorts of scenarios crossed his mind. What if he'd never met Cassie? What if he hadn't gone to the summer ball at The Laurels? He shuddered at the thought. It was inconceivable to imagine life without her now.

Cassie too, had had similar thoughts. That 'niggle' which had taken root in her psyche, had well and truly been pulled free. Now that they had openly discussed marriage, her mind was at rest. Although they had talked about eloping, it had been in a half joking kind of way. Not that she didn't believe they wouldn't marry, but perhaps running away to exchange vows imminently was a touch hasty. Rory was absolutely right, they *would* have a lot on with renovating the barn and setting up a small-holding. Still, Cassie really did like the idea of eloping in secret. It just seemed so… romantic, so… adventurous! The main thing for her, though, was that her future was secure with him. For all her spontaneity, her take-a-leap-of-faith attitude, Cassie did need that rock-solid, cast-iron security. And with Rory she had that.

So, together, in their own inimitable way, they had each found exactly what they had been searching for. Whilst living a more simplistic life hadn't been at the top of Cassie's bucket list, she had started to embrace it. Rory's lips twitched when he saw her impatiently unwrap a parcel of books delivered in the post. Cassie held each one up, *Home Grown*, *Organic all the Way* and *The Smallholder's Aid*.

'Look, what do you think?' she'd asked with glee, face lit with excitement.

'Brilliant. Just what we need,' he'd replied with a thumbs up. He only hoped that the novelty didn't wear off, once they were up to their eyes in muck with no luxuries.

'You must remember,' Cassie continued, 'that I'm a farmer's daughter, after all. It's in the blood. Just you wait, I'll take to the eco way of life like a duck to water.'

Rory laughed. How he loved this gutsy, cute pixie girl of his. He'd never come across anybody like her before.

They were due to meet Colin that afternoon. Rory hoped Jasper wouldn't be about, being a tad embarrassed at Cassie contacting Adira the day after their wedding. Still, it had paid off and now that they knew the barn was going to be their future home, they could start to make definite future plans.

Cassie had given in her notice and only had one month to work. As soon as all the paperwork was signed and the monies transferred, Rory was ready to contact a reputable architect he had been researching, who was well known for improving a building's eco credentials. Once the detailed plans had been drafted for the barn, they would need submitting to the council for approval. Only when (and if) approval had been given, could they then start the building work. He would also have to organise a professional ecological assessment to determine if any of the proposed building work would interfere with the local nature. So much to think about! Rory's head was spinning. It was equally exciting and daunting at the same time, but as he sensibly counselled, they had to take each day at a time.

To Rory's relief, Colin was alone in the estate office when he and Cassie entered. All the documents were neatly spread out on the desk, ready for their signatures. Cassie couldn't sign quick enough, as she sat down and grabbed a nearby pen. Again, Rory had to stifle a laugh. She was such an open book; what you saw was what you got. There were no airs or graces, no hidden agenda. If only more people were like that he thought, comparing her to the backstabbing, social climbing barristers he'd worked with in London. He was well out of it.

'And now your turn, Rory,' said Colin, holding out a pen for him. Rory took it and wrote his name along the dotted lines. There, he'd done it. He had officially signed away his old life and welcomed in the new one. He looked into Cassie's eyes and smiled. She smiled back. They both knew it was a pivotal moment. They were well and truly committed now, there was no going back.

Just then Jasper and Adira came through the door.

'Hi!' Adira beamed at them. She glanced down at the signed paperwork. 'So does this mean we are officially neighbours?' she teased.

Jasper held out his hand to shake Rory's. 'Well done,' he nodded, then turned to Cassie. 'Happy?' he smiled.

'Oh, thank you, Jasper!' she gushed and hugged him.

'What for?' he asked bemused.

'Oh, for… offering it to us,' she gabbled, then went to hug Adira.

Rory gave him a knowing look and mouthed, 'Fever pitch,' making Jasper grin. Both girls gave each other a tight squeeze.

'Come on, a celebratory drink's in order,' said Jasper.

'Are you sure?' Rory asked, surprised the newlyweds wanted company.

'Why not? We've a house full already,' replied Jasper dryly.

The four of them trundled through the frost-glazed fields back to The Laurels. It was late afternoon and the sun was setting. Rory took in the stunning scenery – a burnt orange sky turning to dusk, with the snow-capped hills in the distance. This beautiful place was to be his home. He would have the pleasure of these views every day. Instead of queuing in the smog-filled traffic of north London, to work in an office full of people he didn't like or trust, he would now start and finish his days here, in Lilacwell, with the woman he loved. A deep, profound happiness overcame him, making his eyes fill with emotion.

'You OK?' Cassie touched his arm, noticing he'd gone quiet. He turned and took hold of her hand.

'Never better,' he smiled.

As they entered The Laurels, the warmth from the place instantly hit them.

'Oh, that's better,' said Adira, thankful as ever for the Aga's heat. She reached for the kettle, but Jasper stopped her.

'Let's crack open the champagne, we're celebrating,' he declared. There were several bottles left from the wedding in the utility room. He popped one open, filled their glasses and proposed a toast.

'To the barn conversion.' He raised his glass.

'To the barn conversion!' they all chorused.

'What name are you going to give it?' Adira asked.

Cassie looked at Rory. She hadn't thought about that. However, Rory had.

'The Harvest Barn,' he announced.

Chapter 35

It was Christmas Eve and on cue Lilacwell had received a dusting of snow to help celebrate the occasion. Parents walked excited children through the sparkling white nature trails, in an attempt to calm their offspring down and wear them out. Snowmen stood on the village green, solemnly staring at snowballs being pelted across them. Families sledged down the slippery hills, squealing in delight with rosy cheeks. The high street shops were open till late afternoon, a godsend to all the last-minute shoppers, of which Cassie was one. But her last-minute gift was bespoke and she had travelled to The Cobbled Courtyard.

Ever since Rory had named their new home 'The Harvest Barn', an idea had crept into her head. She was going to have a sign made and wanted Fitz to do it. Cassie had been impressed at the campervan doorstops he had carved for Adira and Jasper's wedding and thought he would do an excellent job in creating a wooden, hand-crafted sign for the barn.

Cassie had entered Fitz's workshop full of enthusiasm. Whilst she'd known Max most of her life, having grown up with him, Fitz had only moved to Lilacwell about two years ago. He was always polite, but quiet and very much kept himself to himself. Fitz appeared to welcome the suggestion of him making the sign.

'Have you any design in mind?' he asked with a smile.

'Well, as it's going to be called The Harvest Barn, I'd like something relating to crops in it.' She looked hesitantly at him. 'Do you know what I mean?' she asked frowning.

'Hmm, how about a sheaf of corn entwined through the lettering?' suggested Fitz. 'Something like this.' Fitz took an artist pad and pencil off a nearby shelf and sketched an outline of his idea. Cassie watched his hand as it deftly moved the pencil across the blank page with swift strokes. He was a natural artist. Within a few minutes he had finished and tilted the pad towards her. 'What about that?'

'Perfect,' she replied in amazement. Fitz had completely captured what she wanted. The lettering was bold, but simple, not too fancy and the sheaf of corn that threaded through it was subtle but extremely effective. 'That's fabulous, Fitz.' Cassie looked up from the page. Fitz just shrugged. He was clearly a very humble artist. 'When could you have it ready? I appreciate it won't be tomorrow,' she laughed.

'No, you'll have to tell Rory that Father Christmas was late with this present,' he joked. 'But next week probably,' he added.

'That's great, thanks Fitz.'

'No problem,' he smiled.

Cassie's mind was whirling on the drive back. It wasn't just the barn sign that had entered Cassie's head. All sorts of ideas were tumbling their way in. Whilst Rory's head was full of planning applications, architectural designs and ecological assessments, hers had been turning over marketing campaigns. The Harvest Barn wouldn't be just a house name, they both saw it as a potential brand. As owners of a smallholding, they would indeed be harvesters, sowing and reaping their very own produce. Obviously they would be living off their own land, but would have plenty to sell as well. The Harvest Barn would make an excellent name for their business. Following Lisa's lead with social media, Cassie imagined websites, Facebook pages, Instagram and Twitter accounts, all with The Harvest Barn blazoned across them. She would record the progress of renovating the barn and building the small-holding and post updates on their blog. People loved that kind of thing, didn't they? She'd researched various sites online and it seemed watching something grow from nothing and transforming into something spectacular was what the public craved. She thought of crumbling chat-eaux being restored to boutique hotels, derelict cottages into swanky holiday retreats, even tatty, old horse boxes into groovy mobile homes. The list was endless, as were the renovator's innovative ideas. And Cassie had plenty of ideas bubbling away in her head. She really wanted to contact the local press, as previously proposed, to get them on board with their journey. It would bring future custom. Cassie knew how Rory didn't particularly relish attention as the 'Climate Warrior' but insisted he ought to milk it. Being dubbed this title had instantly given him exposure, which they could put to good use. Rory once again was reluctant about this, but he did concede that as a business, The Harvest Barn would indeed benefit from all the publicity it could get. And now Fitz had unwittingly designed the ideal logo for it.

As she entered the inn, Lisa was behind the reception desk looking somewhat tired. She was getting noticeably larger now, being six months pregnant.

'Lisa, I don't think you should be standing behind there now,' Cassie gently told her.

'I know, but it's so busy at the moment. I'm just covering for a short while.'

'No. I'll cover, you go back into the office and sit down,' she replied firmly. She made a mental note to brief all the staff of what to expect from Lisa now – and standing behind reception wasn't one of them any more. Though, as Lisa had stated, they were extremely busy now with it being the Christmas holidays. Cassie had always enjoyed this special time in the hotel, the atmosphere buzzed and everyone was in a good mood, which meant good tips, too. It suddenly dawned on her at that moment, this was the last Christmas she would have at the inn. Her chin trembled. She must not get emotional, she told herself. There was too much to do without blubbering with sentimentality. Then her thoughts were distracted by seeing Rory push through the doors carrying various shopping bags. Clearly she wasn't the only last-minute shopper.

'Hi.' He heaved a sigh of relief and dumped his bags on the floor.

'Got everything then?' Cassie asked.

'Yep. The lot. You, Mum, Dad, brothers and nephew. Sorted.'

They had been invited for Christmas dinner at Rory's parents' house, which Cassie was looking forward to. She was keen to meet them and see his childhood home. She knew they'd been briefed by Rory with their plans, so wasn't expecting any awkwardness, and she suspected his parents had long since ceased to be shocked by their son's impulsiveness. As he kept telling her, 'They're just plain relieved I'm finally settling down.'

Rory looked at her. 'Sure your parents don't mind you not being with them?'

'No, they're fine about it. After all they do see a lot of me anyway, don't they?'

'No doubt my mum will get out the photo albums, documenting my chequered past.'

'I'll enjoy that,' she replied laughing. Then she paused. 'You haven't mentioned us eloping, have you?' Whilst it remained a light-hearted proposition between the two of them, she wanted it to be just between them. 'Not that I've changed my mind,' she quickly cut in. Rory leant across the reception desk to kiss her full on the mouth, oblivious to anyone watching.

'You just name the day, Pixie,' he winked. 'And no, I haven't said anything about us running away to get hitched.'

–

Fletcher was surreptitiously pouring himself a sneaky whisky. Jasper had relented and unlocked the drinks cabinet, it being Christmas. He was determined to make the most of it, before the lock and key went back on. Lilly had put the turkey in the Aga and it smelt delicious. She had just entered the drawing room to join Fletcher.

'Three hours should do it,' she said sitting down by the fire.

'What?' asked Fletcher.

'The turkey, it should be cooked in three hours. I'll take it out and then it's ready for you to carve tomorrow.'

'I'm sure Adira and Jasper could have done that,' he replied, taking a sip of his tumbler.

'Well, they're newlyweds, they won't want bothering,' she said, waving her hands away dismissively.

Typical Lilly, always thinking of others and never herself. Fletcher eyed her above the rim of his glass.

'What are you doing tomorrow?' he asked, knowing full well it would be a quiet meal with Ruby in front of the Royal speech.

'Oh just a quiet meal with Ruby,' Lilly sighed.

'Why not join us, here?'

Lilly's head shot up. 'Oh, we'd *love* that!'

We? But yes, of course she wouldn't leave her twin behind and nor would he want her to.

'Good. Then you and Ruby must come for Christmas dinner,' he replied with a firm nod of his head and knocked back the rest of his whisky. Good will to all men and all that, he thought.

Jasper happened to be passing the drawing room and had overheard Fletcher's last sentence. So, it was Christmas with Fletcher, the in-laws, Lilly and Ruby... and, oh yes, his new wife. Dubai couldn't come quick enough.

–

Christmas day was, as Jasper predicted, a whirlwind of relatives and friends. It reminded him of Christmases from his childhood, when The Laurels had been packed to the rafters with family. Fires crackled, music played, wine flowed and the huge dining table groaned with food. All the festive decorations, still fresh from the wedding, gave the place that extra Yuletide feel. A far cry from last Christmas, he thought, remembering the dried turkey dinner eaten on his balcony in the sun. He'd never felt as lonely in Dubai as he had then. He had spent most of the day in front of the TV, apart from when he'd rung his parents and Fletcher. And to think he might still have been there, out in Dubai on his own, instead of back home at The Laurels with Adira and Fletcher.

Christmas morning had been special, making Adira breakfast in bed. Together they had exchanged presents before attending the morning service at church with Fletcher. Lilly and Ruby had returned to The Laurels with them, Adira's gran and parents joining them all later for dinner. The day was full of laughter, again as Jasper predicted, due to Fletcher keeping them all entertained with his bonhomie. It was good to see how the old boy truly came to life when given an audience. Ruby's dry sense of humour was pretty amusing too, adding to the mix.

It was now late afternoon and, after a full day of eating and drinking, everyone was getting tired. Fletcher led snoozing in his armchair, whilst Lilly and Ruby sat watching the Royal speech. Adira's family had decided to go and walk off that plentiful dinner they'd eaten, leaving Jasper and Adira in the kitchen clearing everything away.

'I think that went well, don't you?' He said, passing her a coffee after they'd stacked the dishwasher.

'Yeah, I really enjoyed it,' smiled Adira. She too had been recalling her last Christmas, which had mainly consisted of sleeping, having being overworked right up until Christmas Eve. It was incredible to think how drastically her life had changed – and all for the better. Jasper looked pensively at her, wondering what she was thinking.

'Do you mind that we don't live alone?' he tentatively asked. Adira looked surprised at the question.

'Of course not. I love having Fletcher about. It wouldn't be the same without him.' She frowned. 'Why do you ask?'

Jasper shrugged. 'I'm mindful that we haven't had much time alone.'

'We will in Dubai,' she replied softly.

'It's just that The Laurels and Fletcher is part of who I am. I could never leave.' He looked into her eyes searchingly, hoping she'd understand.

'Hey,' Adira put her coffee down and went to hug him. 'I know that,' she said, kissing his lips, 'and I wouldn't want it any other way.'

Meanwhile, Cassie and Rory's Christmas was in full swing. After having met his parents in the morning and sharing a relatively quiet, peaceful breakfast, in came the brothers later in the afternoon, creating a buzz. All three looked alike, with their dark curls, tall frames and twinkling eyes full of mischief. They must have been a handful growing up, thought Cassie, laughing at their banter with each another. The eldest brother, Ed, had a lovely, though rather timid, wife and an extremely boisterous son, who obviously took after his dad's side of the family. They had been more than curious to meet the girl who had seemingly 'tamed' their Rory, the rebel of the family.

Cassie had loved every minute of the mickey-taking and harmless fun baited back and forth between the Molloy family, fitting in seamlessly. She enjoyed the easy-going way about them and didn't feel at all intimidated being the newcomer.

After all the presents had been opened, they gathered round the dining table, which proved to be a tight squeeze, to eat dinner. Then Rory announced it was time to start the party games. This, apparently, was a Molloy family tradition. Cassie giggled at Rory's attempt at charades, until he pulled her to her feet and said it was her turn.

It was clear to see the love and affection the family had for each other, and Rory's mum in particular paid

Cassie lots of attention, smiling with genuine affection on hearing Rory's nickname for her.

'Pixie?' she questioned quietly.

'Hmm, it's because of my cropped hair,' Cassie explained. 'It's called a pixie cut.'

'Oh, I see,' she answered with a chuckle.

The games continued and moved on to Guess Who? which involved Post-It notes stuck to foreheads with famous names on them. Everyone howled at Rory trying to guess his own name as 'The Climate Warrior'.

When it was time to go, Cassie felt a real sadness at saying farewell. They'd had a fantastic time. As they waved each other off and the cars slowly exited down the drive, Rory turned to Cassie.

'They all adore you,' he smiled and kissed her.

Cassie's heart filled with love for him. Today couldn't have gone any better. It had been one of the best Christmases ever. She looked down at the bracelet he had given her, with a tiny pixie charm linked to it. The Hunter Wellington boots she'd given him looked pretty damn practical in comparison, but were very well received nonetheless – she hadn't been able to resist buying them after he'd told her he didn't have any boots, having had no need for them in London. She was only glad Rory had the barn sign yet to open once Fitz had made it.

'Bye!' they shouted through the open car windows. Rory's parents stood at the front door madly waving back.

'Well, it looks like our boy has finally settled down,' said his dad, as the last car left.

'Thank the Lord,' replied his mother, remembering all the demonstrations, rallies, protests and goodness knows what he'd spearheaded. Now at last she could rest easy, in the knowledge he had met a stabilising influence. The future they were about to carve out for themselves seemed idyllic, a far cry from the tearaway student who was always campaigning on some mission or another.

Chapter 36

From the moment she stepped off the plane into the pleasant evening heat, Adira had been captured by Dubai. The whiteness of the sand, the scale of the skyscrapers, the limitless culinary delights in restaurants with awe-inspiring, iconic views of the city; it was all so much to take in. Jasper smiled to himself, enjoying her reaction to the place which he'd called home for two years. It took him back to his first impressions of Dubai, albeit he had been there to work, not honeymoon. This visit was completely different and he intended to make the most of it with his new wife.

Jasper had particularly enjoyed seeing how excited Adira had been when the plane was landing. It had been dark and all of Dubai was lit up, enticing its visitors. As they swooped down amongst the bright lights beneath them, her face had lit up with anticipation, too.

Jasper had pushed the boat out and had booked them into a five-star luxury hotel on the Jumeirah beach front, with balconies overlooking the turquoise ocean and breathtaking city lines. Everything had gone to plan, just as he expected it would. The hotel staff were attentive, making sure they wanted for nothing – from the champagne chilling on ice awaiting their arrival, to the rose petals decorating their pillows. The room was huge with a hot tub bubbling away on the balcony. Room service was twenty-four seven and Adira had never known extravagance like it. She had gasped when first entering the hotel, such was its opulence. An enormous white marble lobby led to two stairways either side. A gigantic glass sculpture hung suspended from the ceiling, its chiselled fragments capturing the light as it sparkled and dazzled in mid-air. Aromatic incense filled the air, whilst immaculately dressed staff waited hand and foot on its guests.

'Oh, Jasper!' she'd exclaimed when stepping into their room.

'You like?' he'd smiled. This was exactly the response he'd wanted.

After a good night's sleep from all the travelling, they had woken to the early morning sun shining through the balcony doors, promising them a new and exciting day. Stretching, Jasper rolled on to his side and gazed down at his wife. How beautiful she was with her flawless complexion and long blonde waves cascading over the pillow. Her eyelids fluttered open to reveal those gorgeous blue eyes.

'Morning, Mrs Hendricks.' He lowered his head to kiss her lips.

'Morning.' She smiled, then sat up to look out of the windows. 'What shall we do today?' She fancied a lazy day on the beach. She couldn't wait to walk on its golden shoreline and swim in the warm waters of the Arabian Gulf.

'Whatever you want,' Jasper replied, then playfully tugged her back down to lie on the bed. 'But I've something in mind for now,' he whispered, trailing kisses along her collar bone, then up her neck to reach her lips again. Adira wrapped her arms round him and hugged him hard.

Later that morning after breakfasting on the balcony, they made their way to the beach. But instead of having a lazy day there, Jasper took them to Kite beach, which was the super-cool place for water sports. Here, Adira had waterskied for the first time ever. Jasper however was no stranger to this sport and had excelled, with his muscular body moving in sync with the speed boat and jet skis. Adira had clocked one or two admiring glances from a few of the ladies sunbathing on loungers, as they strolled down the sand. And who could blame them? she thought. Jasper looked an Adonis in his black shorts and bare chest.

The evening was enchanting, eating alfresco at an award-winning Michelin-starred restaurant, overlooking the still, glimmering water. Lanterns glowed from the outdoor decking as a guitarist gently strummed. They were in the Dubai marina, which boasted many lavish yachts. There they floated, illuminating wealth and glamour, as if in competition with each other.

'So,' sighed Adira happily sipping her wine. 'What will tomorrow bring?' she asked, knowing full well Jasper would have ideas.

'How about visiting Bur Dubai, the oldest part of the city?' He was sure she'd love the atmosphere of the gold and spice souks of old Dubai, piled high with aromatic and glittering treats.

'Let's!' she agreed with gusto. Jasper couldn't help smiling at her eagerness. She looked exquisite tonight in a fitted black dress, perfectly complementing her slim figure. The sun had already given her skin a soft, golden shine, highlights threading through her hair. My God she was pretty. He too, had noticed quite a few heads turn, but then they would, especially with her colouring. Blonde-haired ladies in Dubai stood out in contrast to the usual dark-haired beauties. He understood the looks aimed his way. He was indeed a very lucky man. This had to be the most content he'd ever been in his life, he realised on reflection. Whilst he'd had an idyllic time as a child with Fletcher at The Laurels, it had only been in the holidays. Those long hazy days of summer always came to an end, with a sad little boy made to pack his suitcase and say goodbye to his uncle. Christmases too, whilst packed with joy and delight, were too short. Jasper had hated returning to school, gazing desolately out of the classroom window, wondering what Fletcher was doing back in Lilacwell. Or even worse, returning home to a house filled with a cold, distant presence and strict rules. Then came college, which had taken him further away from his uncle, followed by university, taking him even further. It was only now, as an adult, that he felt well and truly grounded having The Laurels as his permanent home, with Fletcher there as his anchor. And to top it all, he had Adira too. Together they would make The Laurels a bustling, family home, full of love and laughter. In his mind, he pictured his old bedroom as a nursery for their future children and a comforting warmth engulfed him. His eyes filled with emotion. He suddenly looked up, as Adira's hand rested on his.

'OK?' she asked, seeing him in deep thought.

'Never better,' he grinned. Then he raised his glass and saluted her. 'Here's to you Adira, for making me the happiest man alive.'

'Oh, Jasper.' Her voice cracked and she gulped.

Chapter 37

Rory hadn't wasted anytime booking an appointment with the architect he'd researched. Knowing any plans they made would have to be approved by the council, he was keen to get the ball rolling and the project underway. Rory was confident, having looked at this particular architect's website, that he would understand what he and Cassie wanted to achieve. He'd seen photographs of previous barn conversions the architect had worked on and particularly liked his style and approach:

> A successful conversion will be a sympathetic transformation, reflecting the building's heritage and former purpose, with the interior offering the perfect mix of dramatic, double-height open-plan spaces and cosier areas for much-needed privacy. Celebrating the barn's history while creating a 21st century home is key.

Now *that* was exactly what he wanted, Rory had thought with satisfaction. If they could get this... David Higham on board, founder of David Higham Architects, then they'd be on a winner.

Fortunately he was available to come and meet Rory and Cassie. Initially, when Rory had emailed David

Higham Architects, he had received a rather standard reply stating that David's diary was completely full for the next three months and to leave contact details for when he was free. Feeling somewhat dejected when telling Cassie of this, she, in true Cassie style, had taken matters into her own hands. Unbeknown to Rory, she rang the architects and asked (quite insistently) to speak to David Higham himself. Once (reluctantly) put through, she had launched into full marketing mode and told him precisely *who* Rory was, *the* Climate Warrior, barrister extraordinaire, saviour of the Goldgate Tunnellers. She went on to outline their venture, how they intended to set up an eco smallholding and have the whole thing documented and publicised to the max. Cassie talked of involving the local press, radio and TV, country magazines and hopefully get some form of sponsorship from various businesses.

Funnily enough, David Higham then became available. The mention of publicity made his ears prick up and he sat up sharply, listening intently to this very confident young woman who he suspected was not going to take no for an answer. He recalled the story of the Goldgate Tunnellers on the news a few months ago and he remembered the barrister who had successfully defended them. David was curious; he wanted to meet these two and get to know the people behind the barn conversion plans. And what's more, renovating their barn would be extremely good for his business. He considered all the exposure of working for the Climate Warrior and the pound signs started to flash. His barn design would be covered all over the place, according to this woman. A full marketing campaign, without him spending a penny! The opportunity was an absolute godsend and not to be sniffed at.

Grabbing his diary he urgently scanned it for any possible gaps. True, it was pretty full, but there was no way he was going to miss out on this job, even if it meant cancelling another client – business was business after all. When finally Cassie had said her piece, David Higham, the much sought after architect, couldn't see them quick enough. He was however, a consummate professional and didn't want to appear too keen.

'So you see, Mr Higham, as we're desperate to start up the smallholding and get the crops planted, we need to be in the barn as soon as possible.'

Cassie refrained from telling him that in actual fact, they had talked of buying a mobile home and living on site in it, until the barn was ready. She didn't want him thinking there was no rush, because for someone as impatient as she, there was.

'I see,' said David. 'In that case, let me take a look... oh, as luck would have it, one of my appointments has been cancelled,' he lied. 'How about next week?'

'Really?' shot back Cassie on full alert.

'Hmm yes... how about next Monday?'

'Yes, thank you!' she gushed.

'OK, then. Next Monday it is. I'll have my secretary email you the details.'

'Right, you mean with the time you'll be here?'

'And my fees,' he smoothly added, smiling smugly.

'Yes, of course. Thank you so much.'

'Goodbye, Miss Wright.'

So, there it was, all arranged. When Cassie regaled the whole conversation to Rory, he couldn't help but be impressed. The girl had no shame!

'But we haven't even contacted the local press, or anyone else for that matter,' he'd said incredulously. She'd practically promised this architect a complete marketing promotion!

'All in good time,' Cassie replied calmly. 'That's the next job.'

Rory blinked. She was a whirlwind. But then, wasn't he at times? He'd truly met his match. The corners of his mouth started to twitch.

'What?' asked Cassie, catching his expression.

'You,' he said shaking his head. 'You know no bounds, full steam ahead.' Then he did laugh and couldn't stop. Cassie stared at him, bemused. Seeing him literally double over, she couldn't help but start giggling too. After a while, she wiped her eyes and calmed down.

'Seriously though, Rory, we're going to have to plug the Climate Warrior thing. It's no good being coy, it's too good a marketing tool.'

'I know,' he nodded. At least this time when he faced the media it would be on his terms, having invited them on his land, as opposed to being hounded on the streets of London. He'd have control of who and how many would be involved, only giving interviews when it suited him. Here, in Lilacwell, living on a private estate, nobody could trespass and follow him. He had privacy and protection, without being confronted by all and sundry hurling questions or accusations. But most of all, he had Cassie, his partner, who was more than feisty enough to support him.

'I'll make a start by contacting the *Clitheroe Post*,' Cassie continued, obviously having given the matter some thought. 'And *Lancashire Lifestyle* magazine,' she added. 'Plus, Red Rose Radio, see if they want to interview you.'

'Us,' corrected Rory.

'Yes, us,' she beamed, loving the idea of being a local celebrity. 'Then, I thought of local TV, Granada Reports maybe? I'm sure they'd love to see us.'

Rory smiled, she really was on a roll. 'Why not?' he replied.

'Blimey, this is a full-time job already and we've not even started,' remarked Cassie, suddenly realising the enormity of what lay ahead.

'Just wait until you're knee deep, shovelling muck,' said Rory.

'Oh, bring it on,' laughed Cassie. 'As long as I look good for the cameras!' As promised, David Higham's secretary sent the email outlining the terms and conditions of any possible contract. Rory whistled when seeing the approximate costs acting as a guide.

'He doesn't come cheap, does he?' he winced.

'No, but you said yourself he's probably the best,' replied Cassie. 'Let's just hope we get that grant to help us.'

Rory had secured a mortgage with the Ecology Building Society, who had advised him that, in some cases, local councils would consider giving a grant to an eco project. With nothing to lose, Rory had immediately contacted the Lancashire County Council and was awaiting their response.

Monday soon came and David was due to meet them on site, where the barn was standing. Colin had kindly lent them his office for discussions and any rough drafts of plans they would make after viewing the building.

On time, David Higham's Range Rover pulled onto the field. He'd obviously come dressed for the occasion in his check shirt, waxed jacket, flat cap and wellies.

'Pleased to meet you, Rory,' he said, hand outstretched. Cassie smiled wryly to herself, she had been 'Miss Wright'. Rory's reputation exceeded him it seemed, giving a sense of familiarity to strangers. He turned. 'And you must be—'

'Cassie,' she supplied and shook his hand.

'Right, let's see what we have here.' David rubbed his hands together.

After spending a good hour looking at the dilapidated barn, the three of them went into the estate office. Colin had thoughtfully left them drinking facilities to warm up and Cassie made them all a mug of hot tea and joined Rory and David poring over proposed plans.

'We have approval to change the use of the barn,' said Rory, 'and an ecological assessment is in the process of being done.'

'There shouldn't be a problem, as you're only renovating the original footprint of the building,' David told them. He then sketched out a rough plan following the brief Rory had given him and what they'd just discussed. 'We need to take advantage of the scale of space in a barn, using the minimum of structural intervention,' he advised, as his pencil moved in short, sharp movements. 'A barn lends itself to so much of what we want in a modern home – space, height and massive openings for walls of glass,' he continued. All the time Rory and Cassie sat mesmerised. 'They allow for experimentation in affordable, interesting materials too. Metal, timber, fibreboard, rubber, you name it, pretty much anything goes with these buildings. But the main thing is—' Rory's head shot up with interest, 'not to try and make them what they are not.'

'Absolutely,' he agreed with passion. 'We must maintain the integrity of the barn.'

'Yes,' chipped in Cassie. 'Be true to the building.'

'Exactly,' said David smiling. He warmed to these two and admired their spirit. He imagined them appearing on *his* website, arms wrapped round each other, wearing matching wellies and wide smiles in front of the newly renovated barn he had designed. Yes, this could prove very lucrative indeed. He couldn't resist broaching the subject that had piqued his curiosity in the first place. 'I followed your story on the news about how you defended the activists,' he said looking at Rory.

'Well, it seemed the most natural thing to do, seeing as I am one myself,' Rory coolly replied, caught a little off guard. Cassie discreetly observed Rory's body language, which had subtly changed from being open to closed. He sat up from being casually leant back and crossed his arms. David noticed the sudden change in his demeanour too and was quick to rectify any awkwardness.

'Yes, I applaud what you did there, Rory. Not many in your position would have done the same.'

'My position?' said Rory, staring him in the eye.

'Being a top barrister,' David replied. 'They could do with someone like you around here.'

'Why's that?' asked Cassie.

'Fracking. There's a real threat that fracking could take place in these parts and it's creating quite a stir.' Rory's head tilted to one side. That tingling sensation began to ignite, like it always did when he sensed a cause in the making. 'A petition's been started, there's talk of rallies, too.'

'How do you know this?' questioned Rory, wondering why this architect knew so much about it.

'One of my clients lives in a nearby village.'

'I see.' Rory's eyes narrowed, as though a plan was hatching. He for one, was against fracking. It was dangerous and downright disruptive to the planet.

'Yes, a man of your experience and expertise could prove very useful.'

Cassie's head turned for Rory's reaction.

'But I'm no longer a barrister,' he stated.

'Oh, I wouldn't throw the towel in completely,' warned David gently, giving Rory food for thought.

Chapter 38

Fletcher missed Jasper and Adira terribly. Even though he knew it was only a matter of days before they returned, the place just wasn't the same without them. The Laurels, although still decoratively dressed, seemed lifeless and empty. It was incredible to think that this time last year he'd been used to living alone, with no one to share his home, and it was equally amazing how soon one became accustomed to things. Now he knew, without any doubt, he could no longer go back to living solo in this great house. But then, he'd never have to, a tender voice inside his head reminded him. Jasper would be home soon and everything would be back to normal.

'Tea, Fletcher?' asked Lilly. She'd just finished ironing and was ready for their mid-morning break. Fletcher had been staring out of the French doors, debating whether to potter in the kitchen garden, before his mind had absently turned to Jasper.

'Aye, lass. Let's go mad and have a slice of that cake, too.' He pointed to Lilly's Victoria sandwich, sitting temptingly on a plate.

'Now, what would Jasper and Adira say to you having cake?' she teased. She had made it for their return.

'Well, Jasper and Adira aren't here, are they?' Fletcher chuckled. 'Go on, lass. Just a slither of a slice,' he coaxed.

'Oh, go on then. But I'll have to take the rest home and bake a fresh one. We can't be leaving any evidence, can we?' She giggled, enjoying their subterfuge.

They took the tea and cake into the drawing room and settled by the fire. Fletcher took great pleasure in these moments with Lilly. It was easy to take such times for granted, being caught up with everyday life. But it was times like today, when he'd been missing Jasper, that prompted him to reflect. Lilly had been a life-long companion and a true friend to him. She'd simply always been there, in good times and bad; his strength and steer. He didn't kid himself that she didn't know deep down that his heart had been broken by Alice, but that hadn't deterred her genuine feelings for him. And he had genuine feelings for her too. Lilly was kind, loyal, funny, mischievous and he thoroughly enjoyed her company. Had he ever taken off his rose-tinted glasses where Alice was concerned, he might have seen sense and proposed to Lilly years ago. Occasionally, in the cold light of day, he contemplated this and a sadness swept over him. Then the 'what if?' game started to play away in his mind. What if he had proposed? He pictured the spectacular wedding they would have had at The Laurels, a grand affair, with everyone they knew celebrating in style. Then what if they'd had children? He imagined lots of little ones running around the place, alongside Jasper. They'd no doubt have grandchildren by now, too. It didn't do to be maudlin, he told himself and put the past back in its box, shut and bolted. What happened, had happened, and there was nothing he could do about it now. Except to make it up to her, to *them*, in any way he could. Which is why he wanted to give her the gift he'd bought her on holiday.

He knew the brooch had caught Lilly's eye at the Gem Rock Museum they'd all visited. It had a large amethyst jewel in the centre, surrounded by small peridot stones, set in silver casing. It was exquisite and extremely expensive, hence Lilly's dreamy look when seeing it sparkle in the glass cabinet. Unbeknown to her, Fletcher had spotted her admiring the brooch and had discreetly bought it. He'd been waiting for the right time to give it her. Now, he thought, was the right time, when they were alone. He got up and went to the bureau where he had been keeping it, out of sight.

'What are you doing?' Lilly asked.

'You'll see,' he said over his shoulder as he rummaged to find the small blue box. There it was. He took it and walked towards Lilly.

'What's that?' she said, squinting towards his hand.

'Open it, Lilly. It's for you,' he said gently, putting the box on her lap. She carefully lifted off the lid and gasped.

'Oh, Fletcher,' she whispered, staring at the jewels that glittered before her. She looked up at him. 'How did you know?'

'I notice more than you think, lass,' he replied with a shrewd grin.

'It's beautiful, thank you so much.' She took it out of its box.

'Here, let me.' Fletcher delicately pinned the broach to her cardigan. 'There, you look grand, Lilly.' Their eyes fixed. Was she thinking the same as he? Of what could have been? A lump formed in his throat. He coughed and forced himself to speak. 'Now then, lass, what about this cake?' He sat down and reached for his plate.

Chapter 39

It was the last night of the honeymoon. Adira and Jasper were sitting on their balcony with a bottle of wine. The evening air was warm and balmy and the sound of the sea could be heard gently lapping against the shore. A crescent moon shone down on them, bright against the dark orange sky.

'It's been a dream,' sighed Adira, finding it hard to believe that soon they would be back in the depths of winter in England.

'It has,' agreed Jasper. Whilst he'd loved every minute of being with Adira in Dubai, he was looking forward to going home. He'd missed Fletcher. He'd missed The Laurels and all that encompassed. Running the estate, though a family duty, also kept him nicely busy. He thrived on the job. When he'd first taken over from Fletcher, Jasper was a little overwhelmed at just what was expected of him, but he soon developed a passion for it. Fletcher had been right saying, 'It's in the blood.' It was. He envisaged his eldest child taking over the reins from him in time and then stopped. He wisely counselled himself to live in the present, savour the moment and not wish his time away. Equally, he'd learnt not to live in the past. Not having the happiest of times at home with his parents had often left him with a sense of resentment. But now he'd learnt that harbouring ill feeling didn't do him, or anyone else, any good. Meeting Adira had helped him to live for the day and appreciate each precious memory; and his honeymoon had given them both many, many precious memories. There would be many more to come too, he also told himself.

Adira stared out to the beach and watched the moonlight illuminate the silky waves. It was such a beautiful scene and one that would stay with her forever. She glanced at Jasper deep in thought. How handsome her husband was with his dark hair and bronzed skin. He'd deserved this break, working flat out. The shadows under his eyes had vanished and the rest had given him more vigour. She only hoped that buying The Cobbled Courtyard wasn't going to add extra pressure on him. Now that the wedding was over, she would be able to dedicate more time to working on the estate, too. The glamping business had really started to take off and there was the orangery to host future weddings and events, some of which had already been booked. Adira anticipated even more, once their own wedding pictures appeared on the website. The business looked promising, but it was all time-consuming.

The two sat in a comfortable silence, each taking stock of the future and what it was to hold. They had an early start the following morning, their flight being at eleven a.m., taking them into the UK for early evening. Jasper calculated being back at The Laurels between eight and nine p.m. He wanted to breathe in the cold country fresh air, instead of the hot, dry climate of Dubai. He wanted to stride through lush green fields and relax with a whisky in front of a crackling fire. He wanted to see Fletcher and get back to work.

There was plenty for him to do – the pottery studio and flat at The Cobbled Courtyard needed some building improvements, which he was keen to get on with so he could advertise it as a rental business with accommodation. Running the glamping site, selling the barn, dealing with Fletcher's illness and the wedding had kept him from that side of the business, but now he intended to concentrate more on The Cobbled Courtyard. It basically ran itself, having established tenants that always kept up to date with the rent, though now Jasper had an empty unit needing occupying and he was eager to fill it. His mind ticked over with the list of jobs he had to tackle. Then he stopped, reminding himself he was, in fact, still on honeymoon. *Savour the moment*, that was his new mantra.

The next morning, after thanking the hotel staff and being taxied to the airport, Jasper and Adira boarded the plane home. They sat back and smiled at each other.

'What a lovely holiday,' said Adira. 'I didn't want it to end.' Jasper leant forward and kissed her.

'It's only the beginning,' he answered.

As Jasper had guessed, Fletcher was on pins, pacing the hall like a caged tiger, waiting for their arrival. Hearing the taxi crunching up the gravel driveway, he shot out of the front door. Waving furiously, he stood at the top of the stone steps. As soon as Adira and Jasper stepped out he went to join them.

'Welcome back!' he cheered, slapping Jasper on the back. He turned to Adira. 'You look well, lass. All that sunshine's done you good.'

'Hello, Fletcher,' she laughed and gave him a hug, whilst Jasper took their suitcases out of the boot.

'Come in, come in,' ushered Fletcher. 'Lilly's made a cake for you.'

They were soon sat in the warm, cosy kitchen with tea and Lilly's second Victoria sandwich, which Fletcher thought was every bit as nice as the first one she'd baked.

'Well, is it good to be home?' he asked, looking from one to the other.

'Yes,' they said in unison.

Chapter 40

The snow covering Lilacwell gradually melted, giving it a bleaker, barer look. All the festive decorations were now hibernating until next year and the Inn at Lilacwell had said farewell to its Christmas guests. A quiet lull had descended upon the village after all the celebrations it had hosted.

It was Cassie's last working day at the inn, but instead of feeling sentimental, she was far too busy to feel anything. All the staff had clubbed together and bought her a new laptop, knowing she'd no longer have use of the one issued to her by the hotel. She'd wasted no time at all in looking up contact details for editors and local newspapers and magazines. Then, feeling a tad guilty to be doing such things in work's time, shut the laptop down and concentrated on her final hours at the inn. It was strange to think that in future she'd be on the opposite side of the bar. Cassie didn't find the thought emotional, though, because the Inn would still be her local pub. Had she been leaving Lilacwell it would have been a completely different scenario.

Instead of buying a static caravan to live on site whilst renovating the barn, Adira had offered them a shepherds hut to live in for a few months. Paying rent for a short while was a lot cheaper than having to buy a caravan and was a welcome solution. Whilst smaller, it was a whole lot cosier with its wood-burning stove. They had tested it out last night and thoroughly enjoyed the experience, although Rory had made some comment about, 'the novelty wearing off' for her. But Cassie was having none of it, totally embracing the outdoor life. She'd loved the intimacy of snuggling up in a cute little bed and dodging out of each other's way as they navigated the kitchenette and minuscule bathroom.

'It's so quaint!' she'd cried.

'The barn will feel like a stadium compared to this,' Rory answered.

For breakfast Cassie had cooked them bacon and eggs before leaving to set off to the Inn for the last time; well, as assistant manager at least.

On her arrival, she'd been touched to find the office decorated with farewell balloons and a pile of good luck cards lay unopened on her desk. The nearest she'd got to crying was when Charles, the owner of the hotel, had given a short presentation.

'Cassie, you've been a big part of the Inn and it won't be the same without you.' Then, giving her the present from all the staff added, 'But we all wish you every happiness in your exciting new journey.'

Cassie's eyes had misted over as she hugged Charles, overjoyed and overcome.

'I'll not be far away,' she laughed, still managing to hold it together, 'so no slacking,' she joked.

Now, looking at the clock told her she only had one more hour left before her final shift finished. Lisa walked into the office with a cup of tea for both of them.

'It would have been a bottle of bubbly under different circumstances,' she said smiling.

Cassie observed Lisa's bump and shook her head.

'I don't know how you do it. Surely you must be tired?'

'Only a few weeks to go before my maternity leave starts.'

'I should think so,' replied Cassie, thinking Lisa was getting bigger by the day. 'I hope you're taking it as easy as possible.'

'I am, don't worry,' assured Lisa. 'And when I return, part-time, my training will continue,' she beamed, blatantly pleased to be given such an opportunity.

'We'll make a manager out of you yet,' smiled Cassie with real affection. Lisa deserved the chance to shine.

'I'm so grateful to you, Cassie, really.'

'My pleasure. You'll be brilliant, as a mother and a manager.'

'Thanks. My husband's looking forward to reducing his hours and spending time at home with the baby too.'

'Good. It sounds like a perfect plan.' Cassie was so pleased for the young couple who had wanted a child so badly. She looked at the clock again and took a sip of tea. Not long to go.

'I'm just going to take one last look around,' she told Lisa. Cassie made her way up to her old room. Opening the door one last time she looked inside. It was bare, having emptied it yesterday and it felt strange seeing it so devoid of her personal things. The room had served its purpose, but now she knew, more than ever, it was time to go; time to move on. She walked inside to look out of the window. It was getting dark outside and the hotel floodlights shone over its grounds. The car park was reasonably full with visitors' cars waiting patiently for their owners' return. In the distance the fells twinkled with lights from farmhouses. A line of fir trees ran across the highest, giving a jagged edge to the skyline. It was the last time she'd ever see this exact view. The ringing of her phone pulled Cassie from her reverie. A smile spread across her face when she saw it was Rory.

'Hi, you OK?' He'd been thinking about her, suspecting she'd be a tad sensitive.

'Fine thanks.'

'Ready for a lift home, Pixie?'

She looked at her watch. Just fifteen minutes to go.

'Yes, I'm all done here,' she gulped.

'I'm on my way. I'll wait in the car park.'

Cassie walked back down the stairs and collected her things from the office. She said her goodbyes to all the staff on reception, in the bar and the kitchens, then tapped on Charles' office door to say farewell to him. Then, taking a deep breath, she pushed the heavy entrance door open and closed it behind her.

—

Adira had been busy as expected with the glamping business, but also with the events booked in The Laurels. It was hardly surprising, considering how magical the place had looked on their website. The Christmas wedding photographs were now displayed and really showcased The Laurels, especially the orangery, to its full potential.

So far Adira had two summer weddings booked and a winter one, although she had blocked out the diary for the Christmas week. Even Jasper wouldn't want to have to work that week and The Laurels was a family home after all.

She stared at their wedding pictures, which were truly magnificent, totally capturing the spirit and atmosphere of the day. She melted inside at how happy everyone looked and as for Jasper… he was breathtakingly handsome in his dark grey morning suit. Then again, she hadn't scrubbed up too badly either in her gran's vintage wedding dress. She smiled at the photo of Jasper and Fletcher together, stood shoulder to shoulder, groom and best man. That's one she'd definitely get framed, as well as the favourite shot of her and Jasper, taken after the ceremony when they were all relaxing with a glass of mulled wine in the hall. The photo encapsulated the love and laughter in their faces beautifully. Jasper's arm was draped round her shoulders, pulling her into him and she was gazing up into his eyes. For the hundredth time she thanked her lucky stars that Sheila, her little campervan, had stumbled across Lilacwell. How might it all have turned out if she hadn't stopped in Lancashire all those months ago? Supposing she had carried on, further up north into Scotland as originally planned? It didn't bear thinking about.

'There you are.' Jasper came into the library where Adira had been working. He stood behind her and looked at the computer screen.

'Hell, we made a good advert for this place,' he grinned.

'Didn't we just,' she laughed back. 'We've three weddings booked so far.'

'Excellent.'

'How's it going at The Cobbled Courtyard?' asked Adira, knowing that's where he had spent his morning.

'Not bad, although more work needs doing than I thought in the pottery studio.'

'Really?'

'Yes.' Jasper nodded his head. 'It wants a new boiler for a start and the kitchen units could do with replacing. I've asked Fitz to make new ones.'

'A bespoke kitchen? That'll cost,' Adira remarked.

'It will, but it'll be worth it. I can't ask for decent rent unless the place is kitted out to a good standard. I doubt old Dickie was too bothered about such niceties as new kitchens.'

'No, but what about the other units?'

'Well, Max owns his, so that's not my responsibility, and Fitz doesn't live in his accommodation, he uses it for storage.'

'Ah yes,' said Adira, remembering the charming little cottage in the woods that Fitz had built. He really was a master craftsman.

'The kitchen walls will need plastering too, once the units come out.'

'Busy then?' She got up and put her arms round his neck, then kissed his lips. He pulled her further into his body and deepened the kiss. After a short while she pulled back to assess him. 'You're not too pressured though, are you?'

'No, I enjoy running the estate. It beats having to work for an oil company with impatient clients,' Jasper told her, ever mindful of the stress and strain his old job in Dubai had created. At least here he was working for himself. The phone rang interrupting them. 'I'll let you get on,' he said before leaving.

Jasper was on his way to the estate office where he'd arranged to meet Colin. Entering, he saw the estate manager busy at his desk.

'Hi, Jasper.' Colin looked up from the paperwork. 'The barn plans have been submitted to the council. Rory's just given me a copy to show you.'

'Ah, let's see.' Although he didn't own the barn any longer, Rory obviously knew he'd still be interested in what they intended to do. He looked at the architect's design. It was pretty much as he'd guessed it would be, in keeping with the original structure, whilst adding a modern twist with large picture windows. 'It's good, isn't it?' he said whilst his eyes scanned over the drawings.

'Yes, I'm surprised the architect's got the plans done so quickly and off to the council for approval,' replied Colin. Jasper gave a harsh laugh.

'I'm not. Judging by what Cassie's supposed to have told him, he'll be expecting a fair bit of custom off the back of this.'

'I see,' said Colin, giving a wry smile.

'The sooner this project's finished, the better it'll be for this architect's business.'

'You don't regret selling it, then?' asked Colin.

'No. I'm glad it's being put to good use. It'll make a great home.'

Meanwhile, back at The Laurels, Adira hadn't stopped. After one phone call came another, then another, all wanting to book events at The Laurels, or stay on the glamping site. She suddenly felt a little dizzy. Seeing the time and realising she hadn't eaten anything all day, except for a piece of toast, she went into the kitchen to make herself something. Opening the fridge, she was pleased to see Lilly had left them one of her quiches and plated up a slice. When she sat down to eat, though, instead of relishing it, Adira retched. The quiche didn't taste right at all. Frowning, she put the coffee machine on and ate a few biscuits. Once she'd made her drink, she took it back into the library to carry on working. After taking yet another call, this time someone asking for Jasper, she took a sip of coffee. This made her wince too; it was so bitter. What was the matter with her taste buds?

Chapter 41

Rory was knackered. He'd never known manual work quite like this. He had been determined to start work on the smallholding whilst waiting for the barn to get started and, whilst he still needed the council's approval, he didn't want that to hinder his plans. As the architect had said, he didn't envisage there being a problem, so Rory was bashing on regardless. With Cassie now there to help full-time, they had erected two polytunnels and had sowed heat-loving crops, mainly tomatoes, peppers and a variety of herbs. Then they had built several raised vegetable beds and were in the process of filling them with topsoil and multipurpose compost, which Rory had been at pains to mix together, explaining to Cassie that doing so ensured the nutrients spread out evenly.

Cassie had got stuck in, shovelling the soil into the beds, although after a while did get tired, not being used to such strenuous work. Even so, she wasn't about to stop; she had been as eager as Rory to get their land going. The quicker they sowed, the sooner they could watch the crops grow, reaping the rewards when the time was right. It was ironic for a couple so hasty and impulsive to have to be patient, letting nature take its course. There would be no instant results in this business, just nurture and wait.

January unfortunately meant that Rory and Cassie were limited as to what they could sow but, later in the year, around March, would see them planting potatoes, lettuce, radishes and other vegetables. In the meantime, Rory was keen to prepare as much as possible, having also made compost bins from pallet wood and chicken wire.

'Those two are for the green compost,' he pointed to two large square bins at the edge of the field, 'whilst the other two,' which stood further away, 'are for the brown compost.' Cassie laughed and looked at him.

'You're expecting me to know the difference between green and brown compost?'

'Yes, Miss Wright, I am,' he grinned. 'I'm sure it's all in those books you bought?' Not waiting for her to reply he explained, 'Green compost is rich in nitrogen. We'll fill those bins with grass clippings, vegetable scraps, animal manure and coffee grounds.'

'I see.'

'And brown compost is rich in carbon. We'll fill those bins with autumn leaves, small branches from garden pruning, cardboard and shredded newspaper.'

'OK,' nodded Cassie, then added, 'Talking of news-paper, the editor from *Lancashire Lifestyle* has replied to my email.' She had put off telling Rory last evening when she'd checked her mail, not wanting to distract him from the jobs they had planned. Cassie really enjoyed working with him and wanted to make good progress before letting him know that a journalist would be interviewing them. She had tactfully arranged for the magazine to come the following week, when they had finished most of what they had scheduled to do.

He turned to face her, his expression inscrutable. 'I see.'

'Yes, someone's coming next Friday to talk to us and take a few pictures.'

'But the barn's not built yet—' he tried to protest.

'They're interested in the before and after shots,' she interrupted. 'Taking photos of the state the barn's in now will make it more interesting when it's renovated. Plus, they can take photos of what we've done so far with the polytunnels, raised beds and compost bins. It's the lifestyle they're interested in.' Then she added with a giggle, 'Not to mention you.' To which Rory rolled his eyes. 'Now, come on, we did agree all this,' she tried to reason, folding her arms.

'I know, I know,' he conceded, 'but you can do all of the talking.' Cassie frowned, puzzled by his reaction.

'But you're good at talking. Being a barrister, standing up in court, and look at the way you handled the press, you were brilliant!' she exclaimed.

'Yeah, but this is different, Cass,' he replied quietly.

'Why?' she asked.

'Because this time it's personal. It's about you and me, Cass.' He looked into her eyes. 'Our future.'

'Yes but it's still for a good cause, Rory. Think what an example we'd be setting, living an eco-friendly life.' He couldn't argue with that. Then another thought entered Cassie's head. 'And you're definitely going to be in the photographs.' She went to hug him. 'You handsome brute.'

'Too right,' he smiled, then kissed her. 'Come on, Pixie, let's go in.'

It was starting to get dark and they had been busy working all day. At times like these, Cassie wished she could sink into a hot bubble bath, to soothe away all those aches and strains from the day's digging and planting. Instead she'd have to make do with a short shower in the shepherds hut. Still, it was her choice and she wouldn't change a thing. She was getting used to planning ahead for meals, having become reliant in the past on using the hotel kitchens as and when. That was the one thing she missed the most, just helping herself to any of the food which had been left. Now she had to think ahead for what to buy — and with little space for storage. Considerations like that, as well as living in such cramped quarters, willed them both to plough on and get things done. 'We'll look back and laugh at how we were cooped up in the shepherds hut,' they'd say, hoping it was true. The approval from the council couldn't come quick enough.

Whilst Cassie was showering, Rory received a text from Adira inviting them for dinner. Knowing it would be a welcome change, he turned off the oven. The lasagne could wait till tomorrow. Besides, he was keen to hear Jasper's opinion on the plans he had left for him.

A short while later, Cassie was glad to be relaxing at The Laurels. She couldn't help but notice how well both Jasper and Adira looked, so sun-kissed and chilled out.

'So, how was Dubai?' she asked the newlyweds.

'An absolute dream,' sighed Adira, suddenly longing for the warmth of the sunshine again.

'It was good to get away and have some time alone together,' replied Jasper, giving them a dry look. Rory smiled to himself. He wasn't sure he'd want to share his home the way they did, which then prompted him to ask about the barn.

'Have you seen the architect's plans?' he looked at Jasper then Adira.

'I have,' replied Jasper, 'and I think they're great. He's done a good job, hasn't he?'

'Yes, he has,' agreed Rory, glad that Jasper had given his seal of approval.

Sensing the conversation was going to turn to business, Adira took the opportunity to go and check on the dinner. Cassie followed her into the kitchen.

'You look positively glowing,' Cassie said, looking Adira up and down. It was true, Adira's eyes shone, as well as her hair and her complexion gave a healthy glow.

'Not sure I feel it, though,' replied Adira. 'Keep feeling tired since we got back.'

'Oh,' said Cassie. Then her eyes turned to the three packets of ginger biscuits on the work top. Adira saw her glancing at them.

'I've developed a taste for those.' She nodded towards them. 'Funny, because I've never really liked them before.'

'I see,' said Cassie thoughtfully.

'We're having chilli con carne,' Adira told her whilst dipping a spoon into the pot to taste it. 'Hmm, could do with a bit more spice I think,' she said, adding two heaped spoonfuls of powder.

Cassie's eyes widened at how much Adira was adding. The chilli was definitely going to have a kick to it, she thought.

'Where's Fletcher?' asked Cassie, expecting to have seen him by now.

'He's taken Lilly out for a meal. Ruby's entertaining tonight, so wanted the cottage all to herself.'

'Oh really?' laughed Cassie. 'And who is Ruby entertaining?'

'Some chap they met on holiday apparently.'

–

Fletcher sat opposite Lilly on a table by the open fire at the inn. Feeling the cold setting into his bones on the short walk from the car park, he instantly went to the two empty chairs nearest the inglenook to warm up. Lilly also looked relieved to be next to the heat.

'That's better!' he exclaimed, rubbing his hands together. 'Now what do you want to drink, Lilly?'

'Just a tonic water please,' she replied, picking up a menu off the table.

Fletcher took quite a while to return, having chatted to the many locals he knew at the bar. Old Dickie was there with Max and Fitz, who had given him plenty to talk about.

Lilly was still studying the menu when he sat down. He didn't need to look at the menu, he always had the fish pie when eating at the inn.

'So what are you going for, lass?' he asked, seeing her dithering for choice. Knowing Lilly, he suspected she would just go for one of the cheapest meals, rather than what she fancied.

'Err… the cheese and onion pie… I think.'

'Oh, go mad and have the steak,' he coaxed, sensing that was what she really wanted. He knew Steak Diane was a particular favourite of hers.

'Oh, go on then,' she smiled.

Lilly was wearing the brooch which Fletcher had bought her from the Gem Rock Museum in Scotland. She was very smart in a burgundy woollen twin set and her hair had been neatly coiffured at the hairdresser's.

'So, been booted out by your sister tonight, then?' chuckled Fletcher, who had found it hilarious that Ruby was on a 'hot date' with Alfred. He tittered to himself picturing Ruby lighting the candles on a romantic table for two in their kitchen. According to Lilly, Ruby was cooking them a 'special dinner'. He wasn't entirely sure what it would consist of. Maybe oysters and champagne? They were supposed to be aphrodisiacs, weren't they? He took a mouthful of beer to hide his snort of laughter. Whilst he found the whole thing amusing, he knew Lilly was taking it rather seriously. Her sister's happiness was obviously an important issue to her, but then Lilly was the one that had to live with Ruby, warts and all. Clearly, if Ruby was happy, then so was Lilly, and if Lilly was happy, then so was he, Fletcher reflected. He took in her appearance, noticing how lovely she looked tonight, all 'dolled up' as he would put it, making a change from seeing her in the usual apron and slippers she wore at The Laurels. He was genuinely pleased for Ruby too, all joking aside. Alfred was a thoroughly decent chap and made a good companion for her. Although, truth be told, he was more pleased that it may now open up a different opportunity…

Fletcher had thought long and hard and was going to run something past Lilly tonight. After ordering their food, he decided to take the plunge.

'Lilly, I've been thinking,' he announced, making her look up abruptly. 'Now that Ruby has a friend, why don't we go on that river cruise I suggested a while back?' The question had clearly taken Lilly by surprise, not being able to answer immediately. Fletcher made good use of the silence. 'You could go with a clear conscience, knowing that Ruby wouldn't be left alone. She could invite Alfred to stay for a few days,' then added, 'or even go away with him on a mini-break, too.'

Lilly pondered on his suggestion. It did make sense, now that Ruby had Alfred for company. Well, why not? She quite liked the idea of floating tranquilly along the Danube, taking in all the sights.

'Yes, Fletcher. I think that would be lovely.'

'Good lass!' he replied with gusto, marginally surprised at how easy it had been to convince her to go. He too envisaged them holidaying together, just the two of them this time, without any distraction or interference from Ruby. It would be a treat to have her all to himself. Once again, that pesky sentiment of 'what if' started to replay in his mind. He took a drink then glanced up to see Lilly staring him fully in the eye.

'I would have said no,' she stated.

'Pardon?' Fletcher's brow creased in confusion.

'If you had proposed, all those years ago. I would have said no.' She was looking directly, yet calmly at him, unfaltering. The declaration floored him. So, all this time he'd been contemplating how things may have panned out, Lilly had been thinking something else. He was shocked, not only at her intuition, but by the revelation that she would have turned him down.

'Why?' he blinked, unable to believe his ears.

'Alice. I always knew she was the one,' she replied. Her voice held no emotion, just a neutral tone. Fletcher nodded sadly.

'She was off limits though, Lilly. Me and Alice could never have been together.'

'And yet, she's the mother of your child, Fletcher. Not so off limits, was she?' Again, her voice was still matter of fact. Fletcher's eyes bulged, he started to splutter in astonishment. *How the hell did Lilly know about Jasper?* It beggared belief. As if reading his mind, Lilly continued by way of explanation. 'The night of the last summer ball I saw you, coming down the stairs with Alice behind. It was plainly obvious what you'd been up to.'

'But... but—'

'Then nine months later, out popped Jasper, who, incidentally, looks the image of you, not Rufus.' Fletcher glared at Lilly in disbelief.

'Why have you waited so long to say all this, Lilly?' he asked in shock.

Lilly shrugged. 'To be honest, I don't know. Perhaps I'm tired of pretending, Fletcher.' Then she continued, 'You said to me a few days ago that you notice more than I thought. Do you remember, when giving me this brooch?' she tapped it with her finger. 'Maybe I notice more than *you* think.'

He did indeed remember saying those words, but he'd meant them as a compliment, in that he'd taken note of her admiring and wanting something. Well, it seems she had done exactly the same with him. Lilly had seen him lust after his brother's wife; and more significantly, she had known all this time the secret he and Alice had shared.

Chapter 42

It was Friday, the day of the interview with the magazine. Thankfully, the approval from the council had been emailed to them that very morning, so that had nicely cushioned the trepidation that had started to rise in Rory.

Cassie had checked for any incoming emails early on and was ecstatic to read out loud the results of the planning application to Rory, who was half asleep still in bed, dreading the day ahead. The well-awaited good news soon saw him leaping out of his slumber to see for his own eyes.

'Yes!' he punched the air. 'I'll get onto David Higham straightaway.'

'No need,' replied Cassie. 'He's been copied in, so he already knows.'

'Good. Hopefully the builders can crack on immediately.' Cassie laughed at his fervour.

'They'll need some notice, Rory,' she reasoned.

As promised, Jasper had given them the contact details of the building company that had worked on the barn's gable end, putting it in a stable state. They were on standby, anticipating Rory contacting them as soon as the planning approval had been granted.

'I'll ring them now,' he said whilst hastily dressing. 'Try and arrange a start date.'

'Don't forget, *Lancashire Lifestyle* will be coming at ten a.m.,' Cassie reminded him.

'How could I forget?' he flatly replied.

By the time the journalist from the magazine arrived, they were in high spirits. Rory had liaised with the builders and scheduled a time frame so that the work on the barn was due to start in exactly ten days' time. This gave them both a huge boost, putting them in a positive state of mind to be interviewed, even Rory.

Spotting the journalist's BMW just about managing to manoeuvre down the field and park by their shepherds hut, they quickly recapped a few items previously discussed and agreed.

'Remember, we don't put specific figures on any questions regarding money, loans or grants,' advised Rory. He didn't want anyone to know their financial status, it was a private matter and he didn't want people to assume they were loaded. Not only was it not true, but it didn't set the right tone for what they were about.

'And don't mention Jasper and Adira being friends,' chipped in Cassie. 'People may think we've been given preferential treatment, instead of buying the land fair and square.' Again, they didn't want to come across as taking advantage, but paying the asking price just like everyone else. 'Anything else?' Cassie asked, whilst opening the shepherds hut door to meet the journalist.

'No, I think that's everything, Pixie.' He bent down to kiss her. 'Let's do this,' he grinned.

'Hello, hello,' said a very smart, middle-aged lady wearing a Harris tweed jacket and jeans. Her expensive looking suede boots were lovely, albeit about to get extremely muddy, thought Cassie, who like Rory, was wearing very practical, sturdy wellies. She had carefully chosen both their outfits for the interview, at pains to hit the right note – eco country folk. They wore faded, worn-out jeans and thick jumpers, but not matching. 'We don't want to look like Dicky and Dotty,' she'd chuckled to Rory. Rory's Aran pullover had holes in the elbows, which Cassie insisted was the ideal image. The Hunter Wellington boots she'd given him for Christmas had now been splattered with mud, so that was fine. Her old ones had been borrowed from her mum and had endured a lifetime of farming. So, they definitely looked the part as they shook hands with the journalist. 'I'm Julia Partridge,' she said in rather clipped tones. 'Pleased to meet you.'

Introductions out the way, Julia asked them to pose in front of the barn for some photographs. 'We'll capture the dilapidated condition of the barn, then once it's all renovated, take some more shots to show it off,' she said, whilst snapping away with her camera. Then, she wanted to take more pictures of them working the land. Rory and Cassie were back shovelling soil into the raised vegetable beds, trying to look as natural as possible. Each concentrated on the job in hand, careful not to catch the other's eye, in case they got the giggles. After snapping a few more photos of the land and surrounding area, Julia then took some of the shepherds hut. Rory however, politely asked her to stop once they entered it.

'We'd prefer not to have photos taken inside,' he told her. 'It's our home and we want that to remain private.' Cassie looked at the journalist, who appeared to understand.

'No problem,' she answered, then put her camera down and took out a notepad and pen from her bag. 'So, Rory, how do you feel to be out working the land, instead of being in court?'

'It feels great. I love being in the outdoors,' he replied.

'Then why did you study law, instead of farming in the first place?' Julia stared intently at Rory for his answer. Cassie's head turned sharply for his reaction. If she was trying to intimidate him in anyway, she wasn't succeeding. Rory remained cool and calm, answering her with ease, but then he was a trained barrister, accustomed to coming under fire.

'Being a human rights barrister gave me the opportunity and the privilege to represent some of the most vulnerable people in our society. I hardly think that's been a wrong decision. I may very well continue to use my skills in law for the common good in future. So my studying law hasn't been a waste. However, I've now reached a point in my life where I choose to live a simpler, greener existence and have, very fortunately, met Cassie to share this with.' He turned to Cassie and gave her a smile. She leant forward and kissed his cheek, so touched at his reply. This proved too good an opportunity to miss for Julia, as her hand went down to retrieve the camera on the floor.

'I said no pictures in here.' Rory's voice hardened.

'Oh, sorry. Yes, of course,' smiled Julia innocently. Then she faced Cassie. 'And Cassie, how does living in a shepherds hut in a field compare to being in a luxury five-star hotel?'

'Well, as you can see, it's a bit of a squeeze.' She laughed a little nervously. 'But it won't be for long. The building work on the barn is due to start very soon.'

'I see,' nodded Julia. 'And how is all this being funded?' Cassie opened her mouth to reply, but Rory answered for her.

'Through savings and a mortgage, same as every other couple starting out.' His tone was direct and firm, leaving no doubt that he would not elaborate in any way. Julia took the hint and moved on.

'Do you intend to be fully self-sufficient?'

'As much as we can be,' Rory replied. 'We are installing solar panels and relying on solar thermal power, planting vegetable crops and fruit trees, plus keeping livestock.'

'All sounds idyllic, the real country life.' Julia smiled sweetly, but unconvincingly. 'What do the Hendricks family say about all this? After all, you are living on their estate.'

'I'm not sure they have an opinion,' said Cassie. 'I've certainly never heard anything.'

'Really?'

'Yes, really,' replied Rory flatly, beginning to feel a touch pissed off with this journalist's attitude. Wasn't *Lancashire Lifestyle* supposed to be a family magazine? Full of cheery articles about living in the country? He found her line of questioning a touch too confrontational, or was he being oversensitive? 'And for the record,' he continued, tipping his head towards her pen and paper, 'we paid the asking price for this land. No favours, no handouts.'

'I'm sure,' Julia gave another sweet smile. 'Well, I think that's all for now,' she said getting up and collecting her things. 'If you could contact the magazine once the barn's completed, that would be great and I'll come for another visit.'

'We'll look forward to it,' lied Rory, opening the shepherds hut door. Once she'd left, he slammed it shut. Cassie gave him a wide smile.

'I thought I was supposed to do all the talking,' she laughed, relieved the whole thing was over.

'I couldn't help it,' he said. 'It felt like being back in court, all that questioning.'

'I know,' she agreed, 'but you handled her perfectly.'
His eyebrow rose.

'I can handle you better,' he replied with a playful grin.

Chapter 43

Jasper was at The Cobbled Courtyard, in The Potter's Bolthole. He had been overseeing a new boiler which had been fitted that morning and was now in the kitchen with Fitz. Having already taken measurements for the units, Fitz was fitting the cupboard carcasses, the doors for which were still in his studio, being worked on by him. Jasper had chosen oak wood, along with a matching worktop.

'I'll have the whole kitchen fitted by next week,' he told Jasper.

'That's great. Thanks, Fitz. I'll go and see Max, hopefully he'll have the handles for me.'

Max was making cast-iron door handles, which would really finish the job off nicely. As he entered the forge, Max was busy hammering away on an anvil. He looked up when seeing Jasper.

'Hi,' he smiled, his face covered in soot. He stopped what he was doing and went to fetch the handles. 'There they are, take a look.' He handed Jasper a hessian sack. Jasper took one out and examined it. As he fully expected, it was a work of art. Black cast iron, twirled into a slender hook, so stylish and elegant.

'Brilliant, Max. Thanks.' He shook his hand. 'Have you the invoice?'

'I'll make one out and send it,' replied Max. As always, Max was more interested in creating his pieces, rather than dealing with paperwork and figures. Once more, Jasper was reminded of why Max hadn't wanted to take over The Cobbled Courtyard as a business venture from his family. Obviously Max wasn't cut out for it, choosing instead to stick to his craft.

'Make sure you do,' said Jasper on his way out.

On his return to The Laurels, he was surprised not to see Adira in the library. Usually he'd find her there, busy sat at the desk. She wasn't in the drawing room or kitchen either. He called her up the stairs to see if she was there. Then he heard a door slam. It seemed to be coming from their bedroom. Frowning, he went up to see what was happening.

Entering their bedroom he stood still. Adira was in the en suite, on the floor, hunched over the toilet vomiting.

'Adira?' He quickly went over. Kneeling down beside her, he put an arm round her shoulders and held her forehead. Adira spewed up once more, then taking deep breaths, managed to get up. 'Adira...' Jasper's face was contorted with anguish. 'Sit down, here.' He led her to the edge of their bed. 'I'm ringing the doctor,' he said, reaching for the mobile in his jeans pocket. Adira's hand stopped him. He stared down at her in confusion. 'Adira, you're not well—'

'Please, just sit down,' she said in a shaky voice.

'What is it?' His eyes searched her face.

'Jasper, I think I may be pregnant.' There was a stunned silence.

'But... we've always been so careful,' he replied in bewilderment.

'Not always,' she said in a small voice. Another short silence followed. Then Adira continued, 'Remember your stag do? When you came home—'

'Drunk,' stated Jasper, penny dropping.

'And rather amorous,' she smiled, touching his hand. He turned to look at her. Their eyes locked, each digesting the news.

'Are... are you sure?' Jasper asked hoarsely.

'I'll do a pregnancy test tomorrow,' she replied.

'Adira?' His voice cracked with emotion.

'Yes?' she half laughed.

'I... I hope you are,' he gulped. A tear ran down his face.

'Oh, Jasper, come here.' She hugged him hard. Together they sat on the bed, clutching each other, absorbing the fact they may very well be about to become parents.

The next day, they both travelled into Clitheroe to buy a pregnancy test kit. Adira had carried out the necessaries at home and they were sat, agonising for the result. After summing up the courage, they looked at the white, plastic stick which indicated a very definite blue line, telling them, quite clearly, that Adira was most definitely with child. They gazed at each other. Jasper's mind conjured an image of his old bedroom as a nursery, something he had often daydreamed about – now it was to become a reality. Adira felt an overpowering sense of contentment, like it was meant to be. A wide, beaming smile spread across her face.

'How do you think Fletcher will react?' she asked.

'He'll be at fever pitch,' laughed Jasper.

That evening, following dinner, they told Fletcher their news. After staring, blinking, then picking up his jaw from off the table, his shoulders began to shake with emotion and he let out a sob.

'I never thought I'd see the day,' he whimpered. After all this time; after all the waiting... a grandchild. He was about to become a grandfather. A *grandfather*!

The next few weeks saw a flurry of activity in Lilacwell. It was hard to keep a lid on Fletcher's excitement regarding the baby, no matter how much Jasper and Adira tried.

'Fletcher, it *is* early days,' Adira had gently warned, in an attempt to calm him down.

'Aye, I know, lass,' he had replied, but this didn't seem to quash his zest. Already he had bought several baby items, claiming he simply couldn't resist. Jasper had smiled wryly when seeing the train set Fletcher had proudly showed him.

'You think it'll be a boy, then?' he asked.

'Doesn't matter to me,' replied Fletcher. 'We'll while away the time playing with this,' he said with glee. It was hard not to get swept up with his enthusiasm, especially knowing how long Fletcher had craved for this. To see him so excited was quite endearing. Even Lilly had started knitting in anticipation of the baby's arrival. Adira had marvelled at the intricate, tiny cardigans and hats which she had made.

A part of her *had* wished they had kept the news to themselves, but as Jasper had said, that would have been nigh impossible, living with Fletcher, considering the old boy didn't miss a trick. At least both he and Lilly had solemnly promised to keep it a secret. So for now, all was quiet at The Laurels, business as usual.

Meanwhile, for Rory and Cassie, things were the complete opposite. The initial interview with *Lancashire Lifestyle* had generated much more publicity. Despite Rory's reservations with Julia Partridge's interview technique, she had actually come up trumps. They had filled a double page article in the centre of the magazine. The photographs looked amazing and the image Rory and Cassie were at pains to create had been well achieved. The snapshot of the pair digging the vegetable beds was a particularly good one, the absolute essence of green living.

'They're brilliant!' Cassie said in awe, while reading the write up, giggling at the title, '*The Climate Warrior's New Life*,' and opening line, '*It appears Rory Molloy, AKA The Climate Warrior, has swapped his barrister's gown and wig for a pair of wellies and a spade...*' The article then went on to describe Cassie, who '*was the assistant manager of the local five-star country hotel and was more than ready to embrace the outdoor life...*'

It had been the talk of Lilacwell. Wherever they went, people made some comment or another, reminding Rory of the attention he had received in the past. This time it was different though; he had Cassie by his side.

The renovation work on the barn, once started, had really built momentum. This too had created publicity, with a TV production company contacting them, wishing to follow its progress. The coverage generated by the magazine had spread and suddenly everyone wanted a piece of them. A national newspaper had also written a piece about their 'Eco Escape'; but the absolute icing on the cake was when a top publishing house had approached them, wanting the rights on a two-book deal.

Of course all this attention was good for their future business, The Harvest Barn. Already local shops and hostelries had contacted Rory and Cassie, wanting to be supplied by them. Having a sign or menu stating their produce was from The Harvest Barn would be good for their business too.

The Inn at Lilacwell was celebrating the safe arrival of Lisa's baby. Jessica May was born on a sunny, bright morning in February, to the elation of her parents.

Ruby, not to be outdone by her twin sister's imminent river cruise, had also arranged a mini-break for herself and Alfred. They were set to board The Night Riviera, the nostalgic sleeper train, running from London to Penzance. The couple couldn't wait to travel the coastline of tranquil blue sea, catching snippets of beaches and coves.

It was now the beginning of March and hints of spring were in the air. Rory and Cassie had enjoyed their last night in the beloved shepherds hut, which had been their temporary home and which they had become rather attached to.

'It feels strange knowing someone else will be in here,' said Cassie looking round the quaint little place. Rory laughed.

'It's served its purpose, but I'm glad to be out.'

The barn was ready to move in to; well, ready enough for the two of them anyway. The kitchen still needed to be fitted, but they didn't care. As long as there was water, electricity and a mattress to sleep on, they were more than happy to get in and out of the cramped quarters of the hut.

Their smallholding was growing. They had bought chickens and a goat, plus planted more crops. Rory had been waiting for this special 'moving in' day to put up the sign for the barn, which Cassie had bought him for Christmas. He took it out of its box and admired it. Fitz had done a fabulous job.

'Come on, let's put it up,' said Cassie.

Together they screwed The Harvest Barn plaque to the stonework beside the front door, then turned to face each other.

'Ready to elope now, Pixie?' Rory grinned.

'You betcha,' laughed Cassie.

Author's Note

The COP 26 meeting was being held when I started to write this book. This brought the climate issue to the forefront of my mind, which then led to the character of Rory Molloy being an eco-warrior, doing his bit to save the planet.

Whilst Rory is purely fictitious, his ethics are not. Researching his story line gave me more food for thought. I followed the HS2 Rail Project Protesters' story and found myself sympathising with their plight. To dig an underground tunnel and live there for over thirty days was indeed dangerous to say the least, but surely this was indicative of their strong beliefs and principals?

I couldn't help but smile to myself when learning that the charges against these activists had been dropped. Their trial, which had been scheduled to last all week, was cut short as the District Judge dismissed the charges of aggravated trespass and criminal damage, declaring there was 'no case to answer'.

Now, as I write this author note, London's burning, literally. A heat wave has struck the UK, causing fires across east London. People have lost their homes, houses burnt to ashes, proving the climate issue is very real.

So, without wanting to sound too overbearing or opinionated, maybe we should all consider how we can 'do our bit' to save the earth? Here are a few suggestions:

- Use energy-saving light bulbs
- 30°C wash can save over a third of energy when compared to washing at higher temperatures
- Draft proof your house – only heat areas needed
- Don't overfill your kettle
- Don't leave electrical products on standby
- Swap your bath for a shower
- Use eco settings on dishwashers or boilers, it heats water more slowly, using less energy
- Close curtains at night, it helps retain heat
- Recycle.

Recycling as much as we can all helps to reduce green-house gas emissions. Did you know that recycling a single plastic bottle will save enough energy to power a lightbulb for three hours or more? Recycling a single aluminium can will save enough energy to power a TV for up to three hours or an iPod for up to twenty-four hours?

It is believed that 50 per cent of all food waste is still edible and could be 'recycled' through food banks, charities and making animal feed. Doesn't it make you think?

Growing up in the seventies, I loved the TV hit series, *The Good Life*. Even as an eight-year-old, the idea of living a simpler life appealed to me. The humour wasn't lost on me either. I still chuckle at Tom's generator, run by the methane from his animals' manure, but Margo wasn't impressed and suggested to Barbara that he should see a psychiatrist. Or, when Tom hurts his back and is unable to reap the harvest he and Barbara worked so hard for. Luckily the posh next-door neighbours return early from their holiday and help out. Seeing Margo in her bright yellow waterproofs never fails to make me laugh.

My dad grew a small vegetable patch in our garden and I really enjoyed watching the spring onions, beetroots and potatoes grow. It was such a novelty to pick them and have them on my plate. It must have made an impression, as I'm doing the very same thing now, forty odd years on. I'm also still in awe of those people who run smallholdings in favour of a nine-to-five job. A part of me wishes I could do exactly what Rory and Cassie did in this book – throw it all in and become self-sufficient.

Perhaps I'm being a little too naïve, looking at a simplistic lifestyle through rose-tinted glasses? Maybe it's in our make-up to work the land with good, honest toil. Weren't we encouraged to 'Dig for Victory' in wartime? I think there is definitely a degree of self-satisfaction and achievement from home produce. Although my husband draws the line at home brew!

Lockdown put life in perspective, the main priority being seeing our loved ones. It made everything else seem insignificant. I wish the BBC would remake a series of *The Good Life* to encourage us all to live a more rudimentary existence!

Acknowledgements

Big thanks go out to the fantastic team at Canelo Publishing, especially my editor, Emily Bedford, for her steady steer and brilliant editing. I'd also like to thank Liz Hurst, copy editor, Jan Adkins, proofreader and Diane Meacham for the gorgeous book cover.

I'd also like to give thanks to all the bloggers and reviewers for their kind words and support so far, plus my family, friends and colleagues who have cheered me on!

Mostly thanks to you, the readers. Without you, my dream of writing wouldn't have become a reality. It's lovely chatting to those who get in touch and it's good to know Lilacwell is as special to some as it is to me.